THE MANIPULATORS

Also by Winston Fletcher:

THE ADMAKERS

ADVERTISING

MEETINGS, MEETINGS

COMMERCIAL BREAKS

SUPER EFFICIENCY

THE MANIPULATORS
a novel

Winston Fletcher

MACMILLAN
LONDON

Copyright © Souldern Promotions Ltd 1988

All rights reserved. No reproduction, copy or transmission of this publication may be made without written permission. No paragraph of this publication may be reproduced, copied or transmitted save with written permission or in accordance with the provisions of the Copyright Act 1956 (as amended). Any person who does any unauthorised act in relation to this publication may be liable to criminal prosecution and civil claims for damages.

First published 1988 by
MACMILLAN LONDON LIMITED
4 Little Essex Street London WC2R 3LF
and Basingstoke

Associated companies in Auckland, Delhi, Dublin, Gaborone, Hamburg, Harare, Hong Kong, Johannesburg, Kuala Lumpur, Lagos, Manzini, Melbourne, Mexico City, Nairobi, New York, Singapore and Tokyo

British Library Cataloguing in Publication Data

Fletcher, Winston
   The manipulators.
   1. Advertising
   I. Title
   659.1   HF5821

ISBN 0-333-46221-1

Phototypeset by STYLESET LIMITED · Warminster · Wiltshire
Printed in Hong Kong

One of the saddest things is that the only thing a man can do for eight hours a day, day after day, is work. You can't eat for eight hours, nor drink for eight hours a day, nor make love for eight hours a day.

William Faulkner

This is the story of three fictitious advertising agencies – Pendletons, Adams Coventry McAndrew, and Gilbernetti, Orr and Burton – chasing the fictitious (but large and profitable) Larsons' Splashasoap account. So inevitably the characters and events depicted are, well, fictitious.

CHAPTERS

I
VIBRATIONS

II
PREPARATIONS

III
LUNCHEONS

IV
LIAISONS

V
REVELATIONS

VI
INTERROGATIONS

VII
CONFRONTATIONS

VIII
RAMIFICATIONS

IX
PRESENTATIONS

I
Vibrations

As she scampered between the trees in her underwear the curvaceous young nymph's long blonde hair flowed gracefully behind her. To achieve the same effect on the final photograph, when it was taken, would involve hiring a model with the speed of a cheetah, but there was no point in worrying about such petty details now. Small Paul – looking like a mischievous pixie with green spiky hair and a tiny gold earring – leaned back and admired his handiwork.

'Do you think Runalong will buy it?' he inquired pensively.

'Buy what?' Simon Booth asked.

'This ad. Tom's got a great line. "Naturally nature lovers love 'em." It's a great line for a girdle I'm thinking. Could be another "Refreshes the parts other beers don't reach".'

Simon pushed his fingers through his lank fair hair and fiddled with the knot in his polka-dot silk tie, while Paul began to gild the lily of his sketch by touching-in the girl's face.

'You get the pun?' Paul asked.

'Pun?'

'Nature *lovers*, you wally.'

'Don't get it.'

'Runalong girdles are the only ones as don't leave those nasty dents in your bum when you take them off. So they're good for when you're screwing. I mean your average C2 housewife don't give a toss whether she's covered in creases if she's on her own, does she? But if she's about to get laid by your average C1 sales rep with a pigskin briefcase and a bristle moustache she'd like her big bum to be smooth as a baby's.'

'So why don't you just say that in the ad?'

Jesus help me, thought Paul O'Reilly, I'm sure David Abbott doesn't have to put up with such stupidity. 'Because,' his gentle Dublin brogue brimmed with the disdain he felt for

1

all account executives; and for all clients; and for all consumers; and indeed for almost everybody except a handful of top advertising creative people whom he viewed as demi-gods, 'we couldn't exactly use the headline "Wear a Runalong girdle and get fucked," now could we? The Advertising Standards Authority would certainly not approve.'

Simon Booth and Paul O'Reilly worked for Pendletons, the UK subsidiary of Pendleton Communications Inc, the sixth largest advertising agency in the world, though by no means the most fashionable, nor the most creative, nor the most dynamic.

'Why's she running so fast?' Simon asked, still studying Paul's sketch.

' 'Cos the product's called Runalong, you wally. And she's being chased ain't she? It's the caveman syndrome. She Jane, him Tarzan. Your frustrated housewife will identify in a flash.'

'How do you know she's not being chased by a gorilla?'

'And what would a gorilla be doing in Epping Forest?'

'How can you tell it's Epping Forest?'

'You can tell it's not a bloody tropical rain jungle crawling with lianas and gorillas.'

'Well what's the girl doing running through Epping Forest in a girdle? Is she wearing a bra?'

'What does it matter?'

'The client will jolly well want to know.'

'You won't be able to see. It's irrelevant.'

'Won't be irrelevant to the client. Runalong don't make bras. And they won't want to show any of their competitors' bras, that's for certain.'

Simon's hard-won third in Politics, Philosophy and Economics had wreathed his mind with a constricting logic which the pedantry of most of his clients had tended to enhance. He had joined Pendletons as a graduate trainee five years previously, and had reached the elevated status of Account Executive by the tender age of twenty-six because, he felt, he was particularly good at seeing things from the clients' POV (point of view).

'There'll be a branch covering her boobs I tell you.' Paul's Pentel hurriedly grew a bough from the nearest tree trunk.

'... unless it was a Soopacup bra,' Simon continued thoughtfully, 'because they don't make girdles. So they're not really competitors, from Runalong's POV.'

'It's not your account,' Paul said irritably, 'so I'm thinking you've no idea what you're talking about.'

Tom Nathan's arrival pacified the smouldering hostilities, his rumpled jeans and denim shirt looking as if they had been slept in for several previous nights.

In advertising agencies the copywriter/art director duos are like marriages: sometimes both members of the team are as alike as detergent ads, sometimes they are a union of opposites. Small, dapper Paul and big, burly bearded Tom – often called, by people ignorant of cinematic history, Abbott and Costello – were undoubtedly a union of opposites.

'Simon, my boy, what can we do for you?'

Simon Booth suspected that Tom Nathan deliberately exaggerated his Stepney accent both to embarrass and to intimidate everyone else. 'Well . . . how are you getting on with the new Splashasoap campaign?'

'My boy, you know you mustn't come around 'ere asking questions like that. 'Ow is Pendletons to become one of the bastions of advertising creativity and scoop all the Designers and Art Directors' awards next year if gits like you ignore the very system by which great creativity gets created?'

'But Chris Beaumont wants to see the ads this evening.'

'That my boy is 'is problem. The creative department is under strict instructions to show nobody no ads until they've been passed by the Vicar. It's called quality control my boy. Like they 'ave in sausage factories.'

The Vicar to whom Tom was referring was Francis Kemp-Lewis, Pendletons' Creative Director, so nicknamed because he had briefly attended ecclesiastical college in his youth.

'So when will the Splashasoap ads be ready to show Chris Beaumont?'

'Procedures must be followed Simon. Fuhrer Beaumont knows that. 'E invented the bleeding procedures.'

'Can't you just tell me— '

'Do fuck off Simon.' Paul O'Reilly broke in, 'you'll see the Splashasoap ads when we're good and ready. Don't call us, we'll call you.'

'But Chris Beaumont— '

'If our beloved fuhrer's getting up your nostrils you just send him 'ere to us my boy. Me and Pauly will take care of S.S. Obergruppenführer Beaumont, no trouble.'

Tom clenched his fat fist in a gesture that may or may not have been intended to be ironic, 'And shut the door as you go, there's a good lad. If creative inspiration is gonna come to us in the form of a great Splashasoap campaign that will stop the client from firing us we'll need some peace and quiet. Paul - put on the Stan Kenton.'

How on earth, Simon wondered as he walked disconsolately back to the lift, did Tom Nathan know the Splashasoap account was loose? It was supposed to be a dark secret known only to the chairman, Chris Beaumont, two of the other directors, and himself. Not even the Vicar had been told ('It would be better not to unsettle him;' Chris Beaumont had said, 'it might warp his creative judgment.'). So how did Tom know? Simon hadn't breathed a word to a soul. Except to his secretary, but she could definitely be trusted. And except to Jenny in bed a couple of nights before, and so could she.

Simon did not relish the prospect of reporting to Chris Beaumont that there were no new Splashasoap ads ready yet. Tom Nathan was vile. He'd been just the same at Oxford, a conceited yob. One day, thought Simon, who was a far from vindictive person, I'll repay him for his bullying, I'll settle the score. But the immediate problem, he brooded as the cantankerous lift shook itself down three floors, was to explain the situation to Chris Beaumont without letting himself look like an ineffectual wimp.

Sinking back into his well-worn Hepplewhite armchair, and swinging his handmade James Taylor brogues on to his glass-protected Chippendale mahogany desk, the Chairman and Chief Executive of Pendleton Communications in London re-read the telex which had just arrived from New York.

To: Chris Beaumont
From: Bob Boyne
Your profit projection for this fiscal is not only lousy, it is unacceptable. Will arrive Heathrow 0800 Friday. Be prepared to discuss followin items when we meet.
1   When we are cost poor and making no money in UK, I have great difficulty accepting fuct that you have 243 staff.
2   Stationery, telephone and equipment rental costs should have been cut rather than increased. Please have explanatiog.
3   I thought we agreed no temporary sucretaries for anyone, repeat anyone, during vacations, at budget planning meeting.
4   Do we need to spend so much on pensions? Is it government mandated? Can it be delayed?
5   Entertainment expenses still too high. Let me know who the bog spenders are.
6   Prepare list of people for firing so we can start making money.
With my very best washes and warmest regards.

Bob

Bob Boyne's bark, Beaumont knew, was worse than his bite, but only just. As International President of Pendleton Communications Inc, Boyne was in charge of sixty-one different advertising agencies in fifty-three different countries, and he controlled them with the traditional mixture of carrot and stick: one part carrot to nine parts stick. Having been brought up a Catholic he believed nobody was indispensable. 'Popes and bishops come, popes and bishops go,' he was fond of saying, 'but the Church goes on forever.' Most of his subordinates in Pendletons questioned whether the agency, without divine support at its disposal, could afford to take quite so arrogant a stance. Nonetheless his aphorism was greeted with glee whenever he proclaimed it.

Chris Beaumont, now fifty-one, had been head of Pendletons' London operation for three years, and it was far from being the first such telex that he had received. Nonetheless he felt far from sanguine about it. The tone was a little sharper, a little harsher than that of its predecessors; and Beaumont knew, though Boyne didn't, that the vibes on the Splashasoap business were bad. Larsons, Splashasoap's owners, had turned down the last three campaigns presented to them with no real explanation. Admittedly Splashasoap's sales were below target, but there were a dozen reasons for that. If Splashasoap went, the rest of the Larsons' business would go too: a total loss of more than £4 million turnover. The calculations and consequences spun rapidly through Beaumont's brain: £600,000 gross margin would be lost, that's £120,000 profit before tax, over £70,000 off the bottom line – more pressure to cut costs, more jobs at risk, no doubt including his own.

He felt a wave of depression bordering on nausea well up within him, but smiled a confident Chairman's smile when young Simon Booth entered his office.

Over at Adams Coventry McAndrew – widely accepted to be the most dynamic, most creative, and certainly the most fashionable advertising agency in town – the telephone warbled in the room that Harry Adams, Mike Coventry and Bill McAndrew shared as an office. Harry answered it.

'There's a Mr Desmond Digby on the phone for you,' Janet, their shared secretary, announced from her extension next door.

'Never heard of him. You sure he wants me, not Mike or Bill?'

'He said he wanted any one of you.'

'Insurance salesman I expect. Tell him we're overflowing with insurance. The only insurance we need is insurance against being driven barmy by insurance salesmen. Ask him for a quote.' Harry rang off, lay back in his Charles Eames chair, languidly adjusted the crease in his cotton Armani trousers, and stared through his green-framed spectacles at the sculptured ceiling. £23,700 he thought to himself. Advertising agencies waste far too much on décor, he thought. We've spent over £114,000 already, and Bill and Mike are still spending like drunken TV time buyers scattering their clients' money. Who ever heard of a client hiring or firing an agency because of their décor?

'I was going to give my account to Tim Bell,' he imagined the Chairman of Unilever saying, 'but I simply hated the chairs in his office. Simply hated them. Then I saw Adams Coventry McAndrew's dropped ceilings and ... powee. My heart missed a beat and at last I knew the meaning of love.'

The phone warbled again, shattering his reverie. 'He says he's not an insurance salesman. He's Marketing Manager of Larsons.'

'Larsons?' Harry's tone changed instantly. 'Put him through. What did you say his name was? Oh. Yes, Mr Digby. This is Harry Adams.... Yes, of course we'd be interested ... when would you like to come in? ... Can I check my partners' diaries, I know Mike Coventry and Bill McAndrew will want to meet you.... Yes I realise it's only for a preliminary chat ... how do you spell his surname? DALRYMPLE Peter Dalrymple. And he's Marketing Director ... Yes, of course, absolutely confidential ... certainly not, I quite realise ... next Friday, then, eleven o'clock ... would you and Mr Dalrymple be free to have lunch with us? ... What a pity, another time perhaps ... thank you very much, Mr Digby. I'm really pleased ... yes, look forward to it very much indeed....'

'Janet,' he shouted as he put the phone down. 'Janet. For chrissake phone Mike and Bill. They're shooting the carpet cleaner commercial. God knows why they're both there. Tell them Larsons are coming in to see us. Next Friday eleven o'clock. Splashasoap's loose. Sounds like they've finally got fed up with Pendletons. I'm off to the Caprice for lunch.'

'Where shall we go on to then?'

The phrase struck terror into Hal Burton's plump heart. It was almost midnight, and he had been drinking with Des since just after six.

'Where shall we go on to then?' Desmond Digby repeated, sipping his second large armagnac. As Marketing Manager of Larsons he only got the chance to stay overnight in London about once a month, and he firmly believed in making the most of his opportunities: it was a cardinal tenet of his business philosophy.

'What d'you fancy?' Hal Burton knew precisely what Des fancied – but this evening it was necessary to score as many points as possible, to make Des feel overwhelmingly grateful for every favour granted.

'You're host,' Des parried. He had played the game before.

'Annabel's?' Hal knew that Des hated Annabel's. All those vivacious young things just back from a day with the Belvoir, kissing each other oh-darling-lovely-to-see-you-again in dulcet tones, clothes by Kenzo and Tommy Nutter, perfume by Oscar de la Renta, cars by Porsche and everything by courtesy of daddy's estate. Their knowing insiders' conspicuous wealth reminded Desmond Digby too sickeningly of Leicester, of roller skating at the Granby Halls, of the spiky skyline of grubby factory chimneys and sooty church spires across from Freeman's Common.

'Not really in the mood for Annabel's,' Des replied casually. 'What about somewhere a bit livelier?'

Hal deliberately chose to misunderstand again.

'Let's go into Soho.' He feigned enthusiasm. 'Let's tour all the tatty strip clubs. Wouldn't mind seeing some floppy boobs bouncing about. What do you think?'

What I think, Desmond Digby said to himself, staring at Hal's stubby fingers as they tapped cigar ash into the Italian glass ashtray, is that you are pushing your luck, Hal Burton. One more too-clever-by-half suggestion like that, and I'll go back to the Tara to bed. Which would not suit either of us. 'You know I don't like those sordid little strip joints. Nor do you.'

The waiters were hovering pointedly behind them. A few of the hanging tubular table lights had been switched off. Hal and Des were the last customers left in the tiny tiled Casa Roma. I doubt if the bill for dinner came to more than forty quid, Des mused. Hardly lavish expenditure, with a £4 million account in the offing. A £4 million slug of business would be huge to a small agency like Gilbernetti, Orr and Burton, which wasn't doing too well at the moment, he reflected. We're almost bound to be their biggest client, if they win the business, and that's the way to get really good service from an agency. Des had never felt altogether comfortable with Pendletons: they had too many other big clients, too many irons in the fire. But Larsons would be Gilbernetti, Orr and Burton's biggest, for sure. So the buggers would jump when he said jump.

Hal Burton might at least have taken me to the Connaught, he thought. It was a pity the tatty trat stocked armagnac. If it hadn't he could have made a fuss and rubbed Hal's nose in his parsimony. Despite the alcohol – they must already have drunk half a bottle of spirits and three-quarters of a bottle of wine each during the evening – Hal picked up the sharp edge in Des's voice.

'Sometimes I enjoy the strippers', Hal dissembled, 'if I'm in the mood. Am tonight. Still, if you're not . . . what about the Vanderbilt?' It was going to be the Vanderbilt, Randolph's or The Consulate; Hal had known that all along.

'Yes, let's go to the Vanderbilt. You've hit my mood exactly. What a good adman you are. Paid the bill?'

The Vanderbilt's huge bouncer, masquerading improbably in the high-booted uniform of a Russian hussar, opened the taxi door for them, his bear-like paw almost wrenching off the handle.

'Good evening, Mr Asschshinshk,' he greeted them, ingeniously slurring the name into a scrambled noise that could have been anything from Aarons to Zywicki.

'Evening, Ivan,' Hal replied, unwillingly slipping him a pound coin as a meagre investment against possible services to be rendered. One day, Hal hoped, two decades of greasing Ivan's massive palm would bear fruit. Not that he could imagine quite how, or in what circumstances.

'*Bonsoir*, Monsieur Burton.'

Henri, the manager, was considerably sharper and less amnesiac than Ivan. 'Your usual table, Monsieur Burton?'

Hal wished Henri wouldn't use that phrase. Nobody likes to be thought a habitué of the Vanderbilt, least of all an adman with a prospective client in tow. Henri should know that. It was as embarrassing as its opposite, 'Long time no see', which implied that you were unable to afford their exorbitant bills. He would mention it to Henri, if he got him alone.

Hal and Des followed Henri through the maze of close-set chairs and tables, their pupils slowly dilating in the semi-darkness. On each white table-cloth there was a small tassle-shaded table lamp with a weak red bulb. These blended with the concealed orange lighting around the walls to produce an effect which Hal imagined was probably not unlike the centre of a smouldering bonfire, and not that much cooler.

It was just after twelve thirty, and by the Vanderbilt's standards the night was still young. Along one wall, scattered in pairs and threes among the tables, were girls. Or rather hostesses. Bleached blondes and swarthy latins, negroes and asians, tall and short, blowzy and prim, youngish and oldish; about thirty in all, carefully selected to cater for every taste with as little duplication as possible. A few girls were sitting at tables with men, and a few men were sitting on their own. A six-piece band softly blurred the air with muted trumpet and saxophone, playing tunes for swinging but middle-aged lovers. One couple was shuffling gauchely around the small dance floor: a small man hanging from a Junoesque lady, his bespectacled face looking up into her nostrils, his head apparently wedged firmly between her breasts and her chin.

'*Voulez-vous une jeune fille* at your table?' Henri's French accent was as authentic as Ivan's Russian ancestry.

'Not just yet,' Hal replied. 'We'll have a bottle of armagnac on the table.'

'*Certainement*, Monsieur Burton.'

Hal and Des sat down on the gilt cane and red plush chairs. Peering into the artificial gloaming they took stock of their surroundings. They stared at the hostesses, trying hard to see their faces to divine their personalities. Empirically Hal had learned that, whatever novelists might claim to the contrary, people's faces very rarely gave much clue to their character. A brief experiment at the Vanderbilt – and he had tested the hypothesis with many dozens of initially confident clients over the years – would prove incontrovertibly that the nicest, friendliest, chummiest physiognomy would often hide an insecure, irritable and spiteful personality; whereas the coldest, hardest faced bitches would often be kindly, cheerful and generous. Often, in each case, but not always.

'What about that one over there?' Des asked as soon as they had poured themselves large tots from the calibrated bottle.

'Which one?'

'That one.' It would have been rude to point, so Des was nodding towards a group of about a dozen hostesses. Proper decorum must be observed at the Vanderbilt.

'The negress?'

'No. At the next table.'

'The one in white with a big nose.'

'The other way. Dark, with a mauve silk dress.'

'Yes.'

'What do you think of her?'

Hal did not think anything of her. She looked at least thirty-five, far too old for his personal taste. Anyway he preferred blondes.

'Very nice,' he said.

'Shall I ask Henri to invite her over?'

'Why don't you?'

'Aren't you going to pick one?'

Hal thought about the fifty quid each hostess would cost, plus their drinks, cigarettes, their suppers and the flowers for their hair he would inevitably be coerced into buying. He thought of the innumerable pointless conversations with hostesses he had endured on previous similar occasions. 'I'll pick one later. When I've had a chance to examine the talent. I'm not as desperately randy as you are.'

Hal's double chins laughed heartily to ensure Des realised it was a joke. Des laughed too. He had not heard what Hal had said, the trumpeter having chosen that moment to remove his mute and burst blaringly into 'It's Cherry Pink and Apple Blossom White'. He poured himself another armagnac and summoned Henri to call over the mauve hostess.

'Hello,' she said as she sat down next to Des. 'I'm Vera. What's your name?'

'Jimmy,' said Des.

'Jimmy. That's a nice name. What's your friend's name?'

'I don't know. What's your name, Hal?'
'Hal.'
'He's Hal and I'm Jimmy.'
'Hal and Jimmy. Very nice names. Can I have some champagne?'
'Vera would like some champagne, Hal. OK?'
'Sure.'

Within minutes Jimmy *nee* Des and Vera were engrossed in conversation, while Hal glared distractedly into the gloom. It was crucial for Gilbernetti, Orr and Burton to win the Splashasoap account, and to win it quickly. At the very outside they had four weeks' grace before their loss of Spilch Superstores appeared in *Campaign* magazine. Spilch had been nearly fifty per cent of their billings: over £3 million. If they didn't get Splashasoap they might as well shut up shop. In the previous six months they had lost Dansa dresses and Pym's Male Toiletries: nearly £1½ million between them. Everyone in town was saying the agency was on the skids.

Feelings between himself and his two partners, James Orr and Irving Gilbernetti, had turned sour. Sporadically they split into a pair attacking the remaining one. Sometimes James and Irving gunned for Hal. Sometimes Hal and Irving teamed up against James. But mostly Hal and James criticised, carped about, and fought with Irving. When things go badly in an advertising agency everyone blames the Creative Director.

Irving Gilbernetti, the Creative Director in question, was a fast-talking salesman, great at presentations, lousy at work. It was his job to produce, or to get produced, the ads. Original ads that would be noticed; powerful ads that would sell; witty ads that would make people laugh; clever ads that would win awards. Unfortunately Irving seemed incapable of producing such ads. Gilbernetti, Orr and Burton's advertisements, Hal had slowly come to realise, were corny, plagiarised pap. They should have fired Irving long ago. But it wasn't easy, with his name in purple on the letterhead he'd designed himself. And Des Digby had been quite impressed by Irving, earlier that evening, Hal felt certain. Everybody was, the first time they met him. His hereditary Mediterranean ebullience fused with his Brooks Brothers suits, button-down collars and

Brooklyn accent to convey an image of the ideal American adman – with added adpower, sales increases guaranteed. Hal Burton took a long sip of his armagnac and watched Des 'Jimmy' Digby ogling Vera.

Des had undeniably kept himself looking good, Hal reluctantly admitted to himself, even if he did resemble a 1950s movie star: small black moustache, sleeked back hair neatly trimmed and parted, a big likeable smile, and dark eyes which girls described as 'piercing' and 'mysterious'. Des Digby had always fancied himself with women. Hal Burton, now in his late forties and short, fat, florid and balding, was subject to no such vanity.

Please God, Hal atheistically whispered into the less than sacred atmosphere, please God make Des give us his account. Make him remember all the years we worked together at Beechams. Remind him of the innumerable lunch hours I spent trying to teach him squash, generously disregarding his spastic ineptitude for the game. Jog his memory about the times I alibi'd for him to his wife, when he was off with that secretary in market research. Don't let him forget all the lunches I've bought him over the years, even though he told me each and every time that Larsons would never quit Pendletons. . . . Oh God, I wish I'd taken him out more often. I'd gladly have brought him to the Vanderbilt once a month . . . once a week . . . once a night.

'Des,' Hal nudged his old friend. 'Des, you said you were going to fill me in about Splashasoap.'

Long experience had taught Hal that it was essential to extract as much information as possible before Des sank into an alcohol-induced romantic stupor.

'You said you were Jimmy,' Vera knowingly giggled.

'I am Jimmy,' Des said irritably. 'He's drunk. Gets confused when he's drunk.'

'Tell me about Splashasoap. What's Peter Dalrymple like? What kind of fellow is he?'

'Excuse us a second, darling.' Des stood up. 'Hal and me have got to go to the gents. Back in a twinkling.'

Obediently Hal followed Des back through the maze of tables. The place was filling up, and several couples were dancing. A group of drunken Aussies in dinner jackets, their arms around each others' shoulders as though they were about to get their heads down into a bow-tied scrum, were regaling some pommies at their table with a rousing chorus of 'There's a Redback on the Toilet Seat'. Henri was keeping a watchful eye on them.

'Look,' Des said tetchily as soon as they had squeezed themselves into the minuscule loo, 'I can't tell you about Splashasoap now. If that bint hears where I work, fuck knows what might happen. Be on the phone to Dalrymple first thing in the morning, I shouldn't wonder.'

'You're too neurotic about these—'

'Dalrymple's a bloody Methodist. The very thought of this place would give him a coronary.'

'But she won't phone, why should—'

'Remember Tony Pearson-Clark? Reckitts fired him because of that call girl. . . . '

'That was different. He was cheating on his expenses. . . . '

'All the same. We should've talked about it earlier. It's too bloody late now.'

'But . . . ' Hal mumbled desperately, 'but can't you even tell me a bit more about Dalrymple? What's he like, I mean? What's his background?'

'He's a Methodist I keep telling you. About fifty. Deadly serious. Bloody bright too. Anyway, he won't make the decision. It'll be up to me. He'll rubber-stamp it. Come on, let's get back to the table.'

One of the Aussies had joined them in the loo, grinning amiably. 'Nowhere like this in Kalgoorlie, chum,' he confided, 'not as I've ever found. You buggers really do yourselves proud. There's some lovely pieces of arse out there. I was just saying to Bert . . . '

Ignoring the garrulous antipodean, Des and Hal left the loo. Hal was in despair. The evening would cost him a couple of hundred quid. For nothing. Des was striding ahead, anxious to return to the pining Vera. What would he tell James and Irving in the morning? In their parlous financial straits he'd wasted two hundred quid to learn that Dalrymple was a bright old Methodist. Bloody Des had promised to fill him in thoroughly on Splashasoap and Larsons.

Earlier Des had told him there were only three in the race: Pendletons were getting a chance to re-present but Des said the odds were against them. The real threat was Adams Coventry McAndrew. ACM were pulling in new business with the speed and frequency of account executives buying Camparis in Jules Bar. Hardly a month passed without them announcing another new account win. Without a little inside help, Gilbernetti, Orr and Burton did not have a hope in hell of beating Adams Coventry McAndrew. If Des had really wanted us to win the business, Hal thought, dragging himself miserably behind his prospective client, who moved gracefully and rapidly through the mêlée, he would never have included ACM on the list. The vibes weren't good.

'I'll tell you what I'll do,' Des said over his shoulder. 'I'll send you a photostat of last year's marketing plan. To your home address. It'll tell you just about everything you need to know. The lot. But for God's sake don't let on when you meet Dalrymple. And remember, I'm Jimmy.'

Ralph Isaacs paced around his penthouse office and glared at the Schnabel on the grey silk wall. He moved like a predator, taut with pent-up energy and anger. 'Why the fuck,' he swung on his cousin Stanley who was on the phone but not talking, 'aren't we on the Larsons' shortlist? We've no competitive business.'

Ralph found it all but impossible to fathom why his agency, Isaacs and Isaacs, was not on every new client pitch list going. He was quite clear that Isaacs and Isaacs was far and away the best agency in the world: to that its spectacular growth bore incontrovertible proof. Yet clients often switched their advertising accounts to other agencies without, apparently, even considering Isaacs and Isaacs. It perplexed him.

Though he was still not through to New York, Stanley Isaacs put his hand over the telephone mouthpiece as a precaution before responding to his cousin's question: 'Larsons don't want to know us. That little pig Digby says we're too big, which is rubbish. I'm sure he's on the make.'

'From Pendletons?' Pendletons' ads were crap, thought Ralph, but he had never suspected them of giving their clients back-handers. Though now he thought of it, why would huge clients like Larsons and Marmaduke Confectionery stay with an agency that produced such crap advertising if there wasn't something in it for somebody? That would need to be investigated.

'No, not from Pendletons.' Stanley's mind was less suspicious and cynical than his cousin's. 'Pendletons aren't into that kind of thing. But if Digby's not looking for a cut why are GOB on the list?'

'GOB? Who the fuck are GOB?'

'That rubbishy little shop of Irving Gilbernetti's.'

Only Hal Burton, James Orr and Irving Gilbernetti could have set up an agency without bothering to check its acronym. The week after its launch the *Campaign* Diary ran a wonderfully witty piece on how every agency in town – with, curiously, the exception of Isaacs and Isaacs – was always known by its acronym, and for a couple of months thereafter Gilbernetti, Orr and Burton was the laughing stock of the Zanzibar, Mortons and most of the pubs in Mayfair, Covent Garden and Soho. Irving Gilbernetti was unrepentant: 'It's the first rule of great advertising,' he post-rationalised, 'to be noticed, pick an agency that knows how to get itself noticed.' Hal Burton and James Orr, lacking Gilbernetti's Neopolitan chutzpah, tried to obliterate GOB from their minds, never referred to it, pretended it had not happened.

Stanley was just beginning to put on weight and couldn't get comfortable in Ralph's slim executive armchair, which had been personally designed for him by Tony Snowdon. 'They've got Spilch Superstores,' he said. Agencies identify each other by naming their clients.

'I've heard bad vibes about Spilch. Gilbernetti could be losing it,' Ralph replied.

Given Ralph's reclusiveness, Stanley never ceased to be astonished by his cousin's compendious knowledge of what was going on.

'We should get after it. We need a grocery chain.'

'Spilch aren't exactly Sainsbury,' Stanley interrupted him, 'they've only got fifty-seven stores and three hypermarkets in Scotland.' Stanley Isaac's ability to memorise data was legendary.

'You can always think of good reasons for not doing things,' Ralph rasped, deliberately pricking a running sore which he had kept festering since they were kids. 'Just tell Kelly in New Business to get after Spilch right now. We need the business.'

'We need Larsons more. Spilch isn't a long-term proposition. It'll be bought by Asda or Tesco before long, so we'll lose it as soon as we've won it. But Larsons . . . hello, yes, I've been hanging on for New York for hours. What's happened to this call?'

'So why don't we buy GOB?' Ralph asked thoughtfully staring down at the tiny people and the traffic moving hither and thither like toys, eleven storeys below. 'That way we'd get Spilch and Larsons in one swoop.'

'Because they haven't won Larsons yet, and if they lose Spilch we'll be buying a great big bag of nothing.'

Even after working together for nine years, indeed more than ever after nine years, Stanley found Ralph's impetuosity infuriating – though he recognised it to be the driving force which had taken Isaacs and Isaacs from nowhere to one of the world's top agencies in less than a decade.

'Anyway,' he went on, with the phone now cradled awkwardly between his chin and shoulder, and with his left contact lens beginning to play up, 'unless they do back-hand some gelt GOB haven't a chance against Adams Coventry McAndrew.'

'Not them again! How come they're on every fucking new business list worth being on? Why the hell aren't we?'

Stanley disliked his cousin's accusatory tone even more than his impetuosity. Ralph constantly managed to imply that everything that went wrong was Stanley's fault.

'It would make much more sense to buy ACM than to buy GOB,' Stanley said, and then to his secretary via the telephone, 'Karen, I'm sick and tired of hanging on for this call. It was supposed to be through . . . OK, if you're sure. . . . '

'That, Stan, is no bad idea. Not bad at all. Let's start negotiations with both GOB and Adams Coventry McAndrew and we'll buy the one that gets Larsons. So we get Splashasoap whoever wins. It's what Boase would call an each-way bet, I think,' he chuckled.

'Adams Coventry have always insisted they aren't up for sale.'

'There you go again! Everyone's for sale! We've proved it a million times. Christ, it was your idea in the first place.'

'OK. OK. I'll get Marvyn working on both of them. Nothing lost. And if Larsons stay at Pendletons . . . thanks, Karen. At long last. No, I don't want to talk to his secretary, just get Bob Boyne on the line.'

II
Preparations

'Where's Mike?'

'In a balloon.'

'A balloon?'

'Och, old Aaron Thistlethwaite's a balloon loon. So Mike's taken it up. He's trying to pull Thistlethwaite's business from McCann Erickson. Now he's caught it.'

'Caught it?'

'Ballooning. It's a disease.'

'For God's sake. When are we going to get down to the Splashasoap presentation?'

'Tomorrow.'

'That's what we said yesterday. Why didn't Mike say he'd be floating off in a balloon today?'

'Thistlethwaite phoned him this morning. Woke him at five thirty to invite him to the All England Hot Air Balloon Championships. In Rutland.

'We'll never get Aaron Thistlethwaite's business. When Mike gets there, he'll find a phalanx of McCann's men, each armed with his own bunsen burner and guarding Thistlethwaite against all comers.'

Harry Adams and Bill McAndrew were discussing the new business activities of their third partner Mike Coventry. Bill McAndrew had spent lunch-time working out at Big Jim's Executive Gym; he was tingling fit and raring to go. Since he had been converted to Judaism, and had embraced its dietary laws, he had felt fitter and fitter. He was convinced that the prohibition against eating milk and meat together would one day prove to have a sound medical foundation. It was not surprising, when you thought about it: traditions don't stay alive for thousands of years unless they provide real, if imperceptible, benefits.

Harry Adams, in contrast, had lunched at Burke's with D'Arcy Degavino, and had drunk a glass of port too many. PR corrupts, Harry thought, and absolute PR had corrupted D'Arcy absolutely. In the course of a two-hour lunch, D'Arcy had offered him a random assortment of expensive mistresses, introductions to five major new accounts, dinner with any cabinet minister of his choice, four ingenious tax-avoiding business deals, and a top-secret invitation to join a clandestine consortium of true patriots all of whom were putting up £25,000 in order to hire assassins who would simultaneously shoot dead all the political party leaders – the repercussions of which, D'Arcy assured him, would bring about the restoration of absolute monarchy and sane government by the throne.

'The Splashasoap presentation is Wednesday fortnight,' Harry said. 'We really must get started.' Their initial meeting with Larsons, a few days previously, had gone well – though the three of them had taken an instant and unanimous dislike to Des Digby. Harry lightly touched the button and a thin pointed flame spurted from the Braun electronic table lighter to light his Sullivan and Powell.

Bill McAndrew picked up a pad and wafted the unhealthy tobacco fumes from his face. 'Should we be calling in Gregory on this one then, d'ye think?'

Harry adjusted his Cerruti shirt cuffs so that they peeped out the requisite inch from beneath his Yves St Laurent jacket. 'Greg Hamilton again? Surely we can do a new business pitch without Greg Hamilton?'

Bill McAndrew, like a six-and-a-half foot caber topped with a red head, stood up and walked to the window. He had left Glasgow at fifteen to come south, to make his fortune. From the start he had known what he wanted. To return to the Highlands as a nouveau laird. Ever since he was a tot he had known he'd be a designer of some kind. His sense of style, of colour, of positioning, was instinctive. He couldn't draw or paint, so his art teachers had never understood his talent. If Bill McAndrew placed one word in the middle of a sheet of blank paper it looked as if the Lord had meant it to be there, just there, and nowhere else. When he cropped photographs his unerring eye cropped them precisely, never a millimetre too small nor a millimetre too large. Now, at thirty five, he was far and away the most original and most successful advertising Art Director in London; and he was the foundation of ACM's runaway success.

Behind him the telephone warbled and he turned quickly, moving his tall frame as suddenly as a sprinter breaking from starting blocks.

'It's Mr Degavino for Harry,' Janet called as he plucked the receiver from its rest, and then handed it to his partner.

'Hallo D'Arcy, yes lovely lunch, the plover's eggs were . . . I've not made up my mind on your consortium yet, I'm not that interested in politics myself . . . Are you sure? . . . with a floozy . . . many thanks, D'Arcy. I won't forget you if we get the business. . . . Of course I'll think about it . . . see you soon, D'Arcy. Thanks again.'

'So what did that gangster want? Bill asked as Harry slowly replaced the phone.

'He's no gangster. He's a very good friend of ours.'

'He's a very good friend of anyone he thinks'll be of use to him.'

'He saw Desmond Digby at the Vanderbilt a few nights ago. Forgot to mention it when we were at lunch.'

'So? The Vanderbilt's not my personal dish of caviare, but there's no law against being there.'

'He was with Hal Burton. Remember Hal Burton? The one at Gilbernetti, Orr and Burton. . . . Of course, Burton and Digby were at Beechams together. D'Arcy says Hal Burton bought Digby a girl.'

'So?'

'That's not the kind of behaviour his boss Peter Dalrymple would approve of, I fancy.'

'So what?'

Bill was interested in designing ads, not in dirty tricks. Harry let the matter drop. If action were to be taken he would have to take it alone, and secretly. Neither of his colleagues would approve. Neither of them were sufficiently commercial, they didn't sincerely want to be rich. They said they did; they thought they did; but they didn't. They simply liked doing ads, and seeing their names in *Campaign*, and winning awards, and the applause and admiration of the advertising village. They don't realise, Harry thought, by no means for the first time, that advertising is just a business like any other; and more cut-throat than most.

Gilbernetti, Orr and Burton occupied a late Georgian building in Mayfair. When they moved in, Irving Gilbernetti had whiled away the first nine months of the agency's existence decorating and re-decorating the offices. First he had decided that the interior décor should contrast violently with the architecture and he had the walls painted in shattering wide purple stripes against startling orange, with scarlet woodwork, bright emerald carpets and spotlit lighting. Not everybody felt at home in this décor.

Without admitting that he had erred – 'You limeys are so damn traditional, you know what I mean, on Mad Avenue these offices would be just a whelp, just a fantastic whelp' – Irving had nonetheless succumbed to pressure from his partners and attempted a decorative style more in keeping with the period of the building. Unfortunately so much had been spent on round one (the carpeting had been hand-dyed to Irving's precise colour specification) that Hal Burton and James Orr refused to allow Irving to spend more than £30,000 on round two – a pittance, as Irving pointed out, insufficient to decorate a Beverley Hills' dog kennel.

The end result was less than sublime. The carpet was re-dyed to a colour that in patches bore a passing resemblance to brown; the doors were stripped down to their original but somewhat scarred woodwork; the walls were painted dull buff and curious electric-candle chandeliers were substituted for the spotlights on runners. Not everybody felt at home in this décor either. As Irving never tired of pointing out: 'You try pleasing all the schmucks all the time, you end up pleasing no schmucks never.'

In four short years the London air had discoloured the buff walls, the doors had got kicked and finger-marked, the electric-candle holders had browned in their own heat. Tell-tale lines and wrinkles in the paintwork demanded redecoration, an expense to which Messrs Gilbernetti, Orr and Burton were loth to commit themselves.

'So what if they ask to tour the building?' Hal Burton, sitting at the top of the steel-legged, leather-topped and cigarette-burned boardroom table, was pressing his partners to redecorate prior to the Splashasoap presentation.

'So we'll say everyone's at lunch. Jimmy'll think of something. What'll we say Jimmy?' Irving was unperturbed.

'If we don't mention it, they won't,' James Orr replied, his narrow, dark eyes squinting through thick lenses, his gangly body twisting, uncomfortably as always, in his chair.

'But what if they ask? What if they make a point of it? The creative department's a slum. The wall's still pocked and pitted from the darts craze. That was two years ago.'

'Creative's no more so than nowhere else.' Irving quickly leapt to the defence of his department, wrongly sensing criticism. 'Anyway, it was accounts playing darts up there, when my boys were at lunch.'

'I don't care who was bloody well playing darts.' Irving's silly sensitivity irritated Hal, 'It's a slum now. And it's got to be re-done before Larsons come in. It won't cost much to give it a lick of paint.'

'The whole building?' asked James incredulously.

'It won't cost more than a thousand quid.'

'With overtime and weekend work? Three at the very least. And it'll still look terrible. And we can't afford it. This bloody presentation is costing us a fortune. A fortune we haven't got.' James Orr was all too aware that neither Hal nor Irving had any sense of money. The monthly budget analysis already showed the agency to be heading for a £230,000 loss over the year.

'If we don't get the Splashasoap business, we might as well shut up shop. Once the news we've lost Spilch Superstores gets out we're finished,' Hal argued despondently. James was always fiddling with figures. He had no vision, was always too busy fighting skirmishes to understand the war.

'Look, we'll redecorate *after* we've got Splashasoap. Then we'll be able to afford it.'

'If we don't redecorate we'll never get the bloody business.'

'Balls,' James Orr fiercely slammed the table with his bony fist, 'don't talk such bloody nonsense, Hal. If Larsons like us, and if your friend Des is on the level, we'll get the business. The paintwork doesn't matter a fart.'

'It's not just the paintwork. The place stinks of failure. Soon as you walk into reception. You can see it, you can feel it, you can smell it. Des Digby hates failure. We're competing with Adams Coventry McAndrew, who've just spent two hundred grand on their offices – you saw those pics in *Campaign* – and you're quibbling about a few thousand quid. You make me sick. If we don't want the damn account let's make a decision here and now we don't want it and I'll phone Des Digby and tell him we don't want to pitch.'

James took off his glasses and rubbed his eyes, pushing his long black hair back from his forehead. Hal was being a pig-headed fool. If they were going to invest a few thousand in the presentation, he'd sooner spend it on getting some great ads done than waste it on repainting the building, which the Larsons people almost certainly wouldn't bother to inspect.

'Look you guys, I got a neat idea.' Irving leaned forward in his chair, elbows on the table, his olive skin shining with boyish excitement, 'Why don't we, like, re-do reception and the entrance, and this boardroom, and maybe our floor, maybe not. Won't cost two nickels. Then I'll take colour pics of the rest, carefully lit like it's an ad, no cracks showing. Even make it pretty maybe with a bit of retouching. Then we start the presentation saying we thought we'd save your feet the trouble, so here's creative, here's media and a quick tour on slides. Takes three minutes, zoom, zoom, that's it. See what I'm saying?'

'I don't know how that helps,' Hal said. 'Don't see it. Worst of both worlds. They'll still want to tour the building. Your slide show will whet their appetites. Then the fact that some parts have been re-done will make the rest look grottier than ever.'

'Balls.' James was smouldering with anger. 'You're being bloody obstinate, Hal. It's a good idea. Gets us off the hook.'

Hal saw he had lost. Irving's pointless compromise had

been bound to appeal to James's miserly mind. 'It's a lousy idea. But have it your way. At least reception and this room will look respectable. We can get on our knees before they arrive and pray they don't ask to see the rest of the place.'

'Leave it to me. I'll make it happen good.'

Hal fancied some tea and cakes, perhaps a nice chocolate swiss roll, but the depressing pressure of his belly on his shirt buttons deterred him from remarking that it was teatime. 'Now, having wasted more than an hour on that, can we get on with the real problem. How are we going to organise the bloody presentation? What are we going to present?'

They sat in silence, James continuously wriggling in his chair, Hal staring blankly with his two hands clasped on his stomach, Irving leaning forward, his head resting on his hands on the table.

'You've studied the Splashasoap marketing plan Des sent you. How do you see the situation?' James eventually asked Hal.

'Well . . . you've read it too, haven't you?'

'Only quickly. Not really studied it like you have.'

'You read it, Irving?' said Hal, trying to pass the question on to his partner.

'Sure, sure. Course I read it. Boy, have they got some problems there. Boy have they!'

'What do you think they should do, Irving?' Hal persisted.

'Jeez, that's the big one. That's the big one all right.'

'What do you think Hal?" James asked again. 'Des is your friend. It's your contact.'

'Well . . . ' Hal Burton glanced at his Timex. Just after five o'clock. Soon one or the other of them would say it was time for a drink, and the meeting would dissolve in an alcoholic haze. These days meetings always seemed to end that way. Hal was anxious to get something, anything, happening. 'Look, why don't we get Greg Hamilton to work with us? It'll cost us, but it'll look good. Larsons are bound to know Greg's the hottest motivational researcher in town. It'll make us look big. First, we get some great ideas. Then we subject them to impartial market research, using the best researcher around. Well anyway the most expensive.'

'How much?"

'He'll probably do a couple of group discussions. Perhaps a few in-depth interviews. Double quick. Three thousand quid at least. But it'll give the presentation a backbone. We could ask him to come and present his results to Larsons. That would impress them.'

'Yeah, that sure would,' Irving was not enthralled by the prospect of Greg Hamilton. Research always killed really new, really exciting creative ideas.

'I don't like it,' James said. 'We pay Hamilton three thousand quid to come here and Larsons'll think he's wonderful but how does that get us the account?'

Ever defensive James, never ready to take the tiniest risk, especially when it involved spending money; but having lost the redecoration battle, Hal was determined to win now. 'Then we won't ask Hamilton to present his findings. We'll get him to carry out research on consumers' attitudes to Splashasoap. That's bound to provide us with some material to show Larsons. And we'll use it as the basis for our ads. We can present it or not. As we wish.'

'Can't we,' James asked, 'get him to agree a reduced fee if we don't use his name?'

'If he suspected we were not going to present his findings as his he'd charge double,' responded Hal.

'He's sure expensive,' Irving agreed pensively.

Tom quickly saw, as he entered the Pendletons' main conference room with Paul, that they were all there. Chris Beaumont, sitting two thirds down the long black leather-topped table, in the position that he had de facto made the Chairman's; Vicar Francis Kemp-Lewis at his right hand, lighting his Meerschaum, in his lovat tweed suit, green bow tie, the only person in the room wearing a jacket; tall Flora Thompson, the Board Director responsible for the Larsons account, dressed primly as ever in a beige silk blouse and brown skirt, opposite Chris Beaumont; Simon Booth, her wimpish acolyte, daydreaming next to her; Dave Horrell, the Media Director, whose more than usually florid complexion and perspiring pate suggested he had just rushed back from a more than usually boozy lunch; and Bernie Barnstaple, the Research and Planning Director, holding his heavy horn-rimmed specs at the ready, his close-set eyes and pinched mouth enhancing his well-deserved reputation for humourless pedantry.

The presence of so many of the agency's big guns was to be expected, with so major an account in jeopardy, and Tom was looking forward to the meeting. With the irritating exception of Bernie Barnstaple, he felt he could bully and bulldoze them all. Francis Kemp-Lewis had already seen the campaign and bequeathed upon it his divine blessing; which would not, of course, stop him enthusiastically tearing it to pieces if everyone else (or anyway Chris Beaumont) went against it.

Pendletons' main conference room, like the rest of the agency's offices, had seen better days; but not much better, since Pendletons was not the kind of agency of which Harry Adams so disapproved: all style and no content. On the contrary, Pendletons, as Ralph Isaacs had implied, had a reputation for being all content and no style. Its advertisements always made their sales points in the least elegiac way possible.

'Simple, strong, and sincere', was the agency's less than pithy philosophy, first enunciated in 1936 by Thomas J. Pendleton Junior when he purloined the Smiley toothpaste account from J. Walter Thompson and set up Pendletons in Chicago. This approach to advertising, known universally throughout the business as 'The 3-S Philosophy', gained Pendletons much fame and many accounts until the late 1960s when the fashion for advertising that was 'simple, strong and sincere' – and treated the public as morons – began to pass. Led by a new wave of agencies in London – Collett, Dickenson and Pearce, Boase, Massimi, Pollitt, Isaacs and Isaacs – most British advertising stopped being simple, strong and sincere, and grew more allusive, more oblique; was often witty, pretty and fun. It asked the public to become involved in the advertising process, in decoding the advertising messages, and the public did so with relish. Since advertising played an ever more intrusive role in their lives, consumers, as they made clear in countless market-research studies, preferred it to be amusing and enjoyable rather than hectoring and hard-sell.

Little of this impinged directly on Pendletons in London (though indirectly it ate away at Pendletons' foundations). Highly successful organisations – such as Pendletons had been – cannot, and indeed rarely want to, change their *modus operandi*. Many of those at Pendletons were steeped in 3-S advertising. They had made it work and seen it work. The new wave of advertising was smart and trendy and doubtless, they thought, a few smart and trendy clients would jump on the bandwagon; but fashions come and go, whereas 3-S advertising goes on forever.

Chris Beaumont was far from unaware of all this. He had worked at Pendletons around the world, ever since leaving Oxford, and as soon as he had returned to London to take up the reins he had perceived that the agency was fast losing touch with the competitive climate in which it was operating. During the three years of his captaincy, he had consistently sought to steer his ship in the direction he knew it should go. That was why he pressed the Vicar to employ rebellious young creative people like Tom Nathan and Paul O'Reilly. That was also why he had tried, so far unsuccessfully, to get New York to authorise the £400,000 necessary for a complete redecorative face-lift. But Bob Boyne and his money men, like James Orr at GOB, suspected that the redecoration was an excuse, an avoidance of the real issues. Hence the conference room in which they were sitting had been little changed since the early 1970s and (perhaps in the event fortunately) it had been less than up-to-the-minute even then: brown plastic wall panels on runners, which slid back to reveal faded hessian pinboard walls, lit by heavy spotlights hanging from beige polystyrene ceiling tiles, all beginning to show the wear and tear of nearly a dozen years.

Tom Nathan put the large white cards on which Paul had scamped their Splashasoap campaign on to the table and slouched into a chair. Paul O'Reilly, who was far more intimidated by the occasion than he would ever admit, sat down nervously next to him and the chattering subsided.

'Let's see what you've got to show us then,' Chris Beaumont opened the proceedings. 'Francis says it's terrific.'

'The way we see it,' Tom launched into his ritual preamble,

'is Splashasoap's problem's pretty fundamental. It was launched at the wrong time, in the wrong country, in the wrong way. In the light of which you could say it's selling OK. But Larsons think the opposite. So they're looking for some miraculous new campaign to get 'emselves out of the shit they've dug 'emselves into. So they're looking for something wild and creative. So you can forget your 3-Ss for a start.' The few young creative people employed by Pendletons all hated the 3-Ss and were never shy about saying so. 'Let's get back to fundamentals again,' Tom continued. 'In the US of A liquid soaps in pump dispensers like Splashasoap sell like hot shit' (a curious analogy, Chris Beaumont thought, but didn't interrupt) 'for two reasons which don't apply 'ere. First, the price differential isn't against them; in fact the American ads say they're cheaper than bar soap which must be a load of old cobblers, but still. Second, American housewives, as we all know, are psychotic tarts searching for the holy grail of eternal youth and think bar soaps dry out their hands. I 'eard the other day some of them wear rubber johnnies like mittens when they wash up.'

Chris Beaumont, who had another meeting to attend in twenty-five minutes, glanced irritably at his Jaeger-le-Coultre; nothing that Tom Nathan had so far said – except for the curious and unlikely fact about the mittens – was new, and he was impatient to see the advertising.

'But over here Splashasoap's at least eight times as dear per wash as your Lux or Camay, and our brave British 'ousewives don't give a toss about calloused hands, a fact to which the bruised parts of many a British husband will readily bear witness—'

'I'm sorry to interrupt you,' Chris intervened, 'but I've got to go in about twenty minutes.'

'Oh. I thought keeping the Splashasoap account was the most important thing on the agency's work list right now, but still.'

Tom Nathan was right, as Chris Beaumont well knew; but another client had insisted on fixing a meeting at three fifteen, and insisted on him being present. More worryingly, how on earth did Tom Nathan know the account was loose? If Nathan knew, then probably everyone in the agency knew, which meant that somebody was bound to leak it to *Campaign.* And Chris still hadn't told Bob Boyne.

'Now up till now, as we all know, we've been selling Splashasoap against bar soaps on a cleanliness platform: "Gunge and grime go away when you use Splashasoap every day!" A perfect 3-S slogan if I may say so. And all wrong, in me and Pauly's opinion. You can't justify Splashasoap's price premium on an anti-gunge spiel. If we're gonna get British housewives to use Splashasoap we're gonna have to make 'em as psychotic about their hands as the Yankee tarts. So here's me and Pauly's idea.' Tom at last displayed the largest of the cards on which Paul had sketched a storyboard of twelve television frames depicting the action of the commercial.

'We 'ave to convince the 'ousewife that bar soaps make her hands look like old prunes but Splashasoap'll keep them soft and young and lovely forever. Except we can't say that 'cos the IBA will give us hassle. So, OK, we open on a beautiful English country panorama, probably in the Cotswolds, all lush and green (How are we going to film this in October? wondered Flora Thompson) but it's pissing down, bucketing, with lightning and thunder (Lightning has frightening psychological connotations, thought Bernie Barnstaple), and walking through a leafy glade in the rain is this beautiful bird, about thirty, blonde, in a mac (Sounds like the Runalong ad with added rain, mused Simon Booth) but no umbrella or anything.

'So she's soaked, but beautiful, and the sound effects are rain and thunder for the first seven seconds as the camera follows her, threading her way through the wet branches and leaves (She'll die of pneumonia, brooded Dave Horrell, wishing he hadn't had to leave his lunch early), and then a male voice-over says, "Plants need moisture to keep fresh and healthy, lots of moisture," and then, quite suddenly, the girl slips and falls on her hands, nothing dangerous because she quickly gets up but it's made her hands muddy, and the camera closes up on them as the voice-over goes on, "Your hands need moisture too. But the moisture they need isn't water . . . " and then she comes to a beautiful old water pump, probably late Victorian, eh Paul, with a dirty old gungy bit of soap somewhere on it "... because water and soap don't moisturise, they dry your skin, making lines and wrinkles..." And then there's this finger flash of lightning (Oh dear, not more lightning worried Bernie Barnstable, and Oh dear, how are we going to organise all this lightning? worried Flora Thompson) and the flash illuminates a Splashasoap pack, lying on its side by the pump, which she picks up, and squirts on her muddy hands, and the voice-over says dramatically... Hang on, I've lost my place....'

Tom had been moving his finger along the twelve sketches and reading the script underneath them to help his audience follow the storyline; but only Flora Thompson was close enough to be able to decipher Paul's rough hieroglyphs, and none of the rest were even bothering to try.

'... Yes, this is it, "Because water and soap don't moisturise, they dry your skin, making lines and wrinkles..."

'You've said that once,' interrupted Dave Horrell, who was slipping into a post-prandial doze and struggling to keep himself awake.

'I'm just recapping;' Tom hissed, and continued, 'so as the lightning illuminates the Splashasoap pack, which is looking great, glistening with rain drips and so on, eh Paul? The voice-over goes on, "But Splashasoap keeps your hands soft and young..." and the bird picks up the pack and squirts some on her muddy hands and then puts the pack down next to the pump – and this is the bit that's never been done before, so it'll have amazin' impact – and as the voice-over says "... because Splashasoap's a smashin' soap" the lightning seems to strike the pack and it explodes. Of course we'd have to build a model and detonate it, and the final freeze frame is the pack exploding as the title comes up "Splashasoap – a smashin' soap!" Get it?'

There was a moment's silence.

'Excuse me,' said Simon Booth, apologising because he somehow felt that he shouldn't be the first to speak, 'but are you spelling smashing without a "g"? I don't think it's right from the client's POV. Peter Dalrymple's a bit pedantic.'

'Is that your only comment?' Tom asked.

'Well...'

'Well I'm glad you've got straight to the 'eart of the matter, my boy. Course there's no "g". If we put in the "g" it's crap. Uncreative crap. Are we gonna try to please the client or do creative advertising? That's what's fucked up this agency for the last ten years, but still. Everything's been done to please the client. I thought we were trying to change all that? If you want some shit to please the pedantic Pete you can write it yourself. Oh, and I forgot, behind the voice and sound effects all the way through there'll be Beethovan's *Pastoral*, only arranged and played by OMD.'

'OMD?' Flora Thompson's Cheltenham tones inquired uncertainly.

'Orchestral Manoeuvres in the Dark,' Paul O'Reilly chipped in, his thin voice despairing at their ignorance.

'Well, I'm a bit in the dark myself,' Chris Beaumont admitted. Despite his determination to encourage way-out creative advertising, after a lifetime in Pendletons he felt altogether more comfortable with ads that were simple, strong and sincere; and he lacked the personal criteria by which to judge the smashin' commercial. 'I don't see why she's walking about in the countryside in the rain,' he said.

'And market research proves housewives are frightened by lightning; I don't think we can have any lightning,' quickly added Bernard Barnstaple in his nasal whine, putting on his glasses authoritatively, as if to settle the matter.

'Couldn't we just have a housewife in a kitchen, maybe with her sister or daughter? Or her grandma?' Flora Thompson joined in. 'That would be nice, a really nice lovable grandma, how about that?'

'Not another two Cs in a K commercial!' Tom Nathan said with scorn.

'Two Cs in a K?'

'Two cunts in a kitchen. Being simple, strong and sincere of course, and talkin' like prats. "Have you tried wonderful Splashasoap? It's so kind to my hands, I do recommend it. You should try it. I must try some, your hands do look so lovely, could it be Splashasoap's magic ingredient that keeps them so nice and soft...?" Tom Nathan mimicked, adding an American twinge to his accent. 'God protect us from another two Cs in a K commercial. If it's shot by Paul Weiland or Ridley

Scott, me and Pauly's film will scoop every creative award going. And they'll sell so much Splashasoap Larsons won't know what's hit 'em. What do you think, Francis?'

Creative Director Francis Kemp-Lewis had, as he would put it, been keeping his powder dry. He undid his green bow tie and let it hang loose. He had already, at a previous meeting, after an interminable wrangle, and much to their chagrin, forced Tom and Paul to add most of the explanatory copy. In their original effort the voice-over had merely said, 'There's bar soaps. And there's Splashasoap. The smashin' soap.' Somewhat derivative of Levis jeans, Francis had felt. Now he could see that Chris Beaumont was uncertain, that Flora Thompson was very hesitant, and that Bernie Barnstaple was adamantly hostile.

'Well I think it's bloody great,' Dave Horrell expostulated suddenly while Francis was still fiddling with his tie, bringing Tom and Paul succour from an unexpected source. 'Bloody great. A bit original and exciting. My wife would like that. Make a change from the crap we usually produce here. Bloody great in my opinion. Even if I am only a humble media buyer.'

Dave Horrell's intervention, Francis realised instantly, would completely change the balance of the meeting. While, as Media Director, his opinions of creative work were theoretically irrelevant and ill-informed, his apparently naïve 'man-in-the-street' reaction would sway Chris, and probably Flora too. If Dave Horrell spontaneously reacted with enthusiasm then, Chris and Flora would conclude, the Larsons people would probably do likewise.

'I think it's pretty good too,' Francis then intoned in his best ecclesiastical voice, and went on as though delivering a sermon, 'It's on strategy. It's creative. And it is even, in its own way, and I know Tom and Paul will not necessarily agree with me here, though perhaps they will, quite simple, sincere and – I am sure we would *all* agree here – very strong, very strong indeed.'

'But is it really on strategy?' Chris Beaumont asked, now warming to the commercial in the light of his colleagues' convictions. 'What is the creative strategy Simon? We should have begun by defining the strategy you know.'

With the fingers of his left hand running through his hair, Simon started to shuffle the papers in front of him, searching for the creative strategy document, but meanwhile Tom began speaking again.

'We've changed the strategy, I told you. The old strategy was anti-gunge. That's bullshit. That's why we've changed to moisturising. Now we've got a great ad, anyone can write the strategy. Even you, Simon.'

Simon's furious glare went unnoticed as Bernie Barnstaple, beating the air with his spectacles, returned once more to the attack. 'I've told you lightning's frightening. It's got all kinds of meanings. And that pack exploding at the end. The client won't like it. Nor will housewives. I've seen wads of research that proves it, I'm telling you.'

In their rapid conversion to the campaign Chris and Flora had both forgotten the exploding pack which, like Bernie, they were sure the client would never accept. Only an exceedingly imaginative, not to say foolhardy, client – a client in love with the notion of creativity in advertising – would allow his pack to be blown up; and nobody could accuse Larsons of being exceedingly imaginative, nor in love with the notion of creativity in advertising (though naturally both Desmond Digby and Peter Dalrymple would dispute it).

'Don't give us that psychological bullshit, Bernie.' Scenting victory Tom Nathan decided to attack the Research and Planning Director, despite his seniority. 'Of course people are scared of lightnin' when it's the real thing. So am I. So would you be if you weren't stuffed with statistics. But in movies and on telly they see it every night. Like McCluhan says, the medium is the message.'

'And it's the lightnin' makes it so creative, I'm thinking,' Paul seconded his partner, anxious not to be left out.

'Well,' Barnstaple, angry at being contradicted and angrier still at being called Bernie by Tom Nathan, turned to Chris Beaumont, 'I'm warning you that as it stands that commercial is a disaster. It'll lose us the account. And if by chance it doesn't lose us the account and it runs, it will kill Splashasoap stone dead within months.'

'That's what they said about the Brooke Bond chimps,' Tom countered.

'I don't give a stuffed whatsit about the Brooke Bond chimps,' Barnstaple's glasses were now back low on his nose and he was glaring angrily over them. 'Lightning and exploding packs are bad news, I'm telling you.'

Chris Beaumont glanced at his watch. He was already late for his next meeting. 'Look,' he said, standing up to leave, 'let's research it. We've got time before the presentation. Let's see what the punters make of it. Meanwhile, Francis, you'd better get another team working on a back-up contingency campaign. But I like this one. I think we should go with it, if it researches OK. Well done Tom, well done Paul. It's great to see us creating some great stuff for a change. I've an idea.' He turned to Bernie Barnstaple as he reached the door, 'Let's get that chap whatshisname to do the research. You know, the one everyone says is so good. Greg Hamilton. That's it. Get Greg Hamilton on the case.'

'Are you sure we were right to let Pendletons repitch, Desmond?' Peter Dalrymple was a devout man who tried to be scrupulously fair in all his business dealings – a characteristic which Des Digby, among others, was adept at exploiting.

'It wouldn't have been fair to refuse,' Des replied, 'after all the years they've worked with us.'

They were sitting in Peter Dalrymple's open-plan office, in Larsons' modern Peterborough office block. Larsons' management philosophy insisted that all staff were equal, and that individual offices – with their different sizes and accoutrements – inevitably implied hierarchy and status. Despite which, the boss of each of Larsons' divisions usually managed to find a corner of open-plan floor space which somehow communicated to everyone else that he was boss. Similarly, Larsons' management philosophy insisted that all staff and executives should eat in the same canteen at lunch-time, but somehow the executives always gravitated to the same tables, which the staff never trespassed: the top executives sat at the table with the boss, and the middle-level executives sat with the other middle-level executives, and the junior executives sat with the other junior executives.

'I was very impressed with Adams Coventry McAndrew,' Dalrymple continued, 'the work they've done for the Luton

Development Corporation, and for Skoda, was all excellent. First class.'

'People say they're the best agency in London. That's why I put them on our list.'

'Yes. That's why I feel it's a bit unfair to Pendletons. We know what they can do, we've worked with them long enough. They're not up to ACM's speed, not at all. That Bill McAndrew seems a very nice chap, too.'

'Best Art Director in town. No two ways about it. But we've got to make them fight for the business. And Pendletons have been employing some bright young sparks you've not met yet. Chris Beaumont's been shaking them up a bit. I think we'll be surprised when we see their presentation.'

'What about this other agency you've put on the list? Gilbernetti, Orr and Burton. I say, Desmond, have you noticed their first letters spell GOB? Seems a bit unfortunate, that. Do you think they realise it?'

'They did it deliberately, sir,' Des lied. Even after working with Peter Dalrymple for two years Des had still not established the right way to address him. Des hated calling him 'sir' but did so when he felt threatened; 'Peter' was altogether too chummy for a boss fifteen years his senior; and Mr Dalrymple was out of the question. 'They felt it would help make them famous within the agency business. And it's certainly worked.'

'Really? I'd never heard of them before. Are you sure I needn't visit them before their presentation?'

'I went in to inspect them' – inspect was a word Des thought Peter would like – 'while you were away, to save time. They're a good crowd. And of course I've known Hal Burton since we were at Beechams together, and he's a man with a first-class brain. Got a first in Greats at Oxford I think.' That should silence the pompous old fart, he thought.

'This is an important decision for us, Desmond.'

'You're too right . . . sir.'

After he'd left Cambridge in the early fifties, Peter Dalrymple had, for the first dozen years, been astonishingly successful, promoted quickly from graduate trainee through to Marketing Manager at thirty-four by Reckitts in Hull, and then sent to

Harvard Business School for a year as a fast-rising executive with star potential and an outstanding career ahead of him. Yet after he returned from Harvard, for no reason that anyone could discern, his progress slowed down. He had now been Marketing Director of Larsons for seven years, and although he was only fifty-three there seemed little prospect of him being promoted further.

Dalrymple swung round in his nondescript chair and looked out of the window at the Thomas Cook building across the estate. Cooks had headhunted him three years ago and he had turned them down. Now he regretted it. 'There's a lot hanging on the success of Splashasoap, you know, and it's still losing money. We've over two hundred people employed in the Sheffield plant. And there's enough unemployment up there anyway. We mustn't cause any more. We just mustn't. It's carrying some of the sales force overheads too.' And my own future with Larsons, quite probably, he reflected, though it was an ignoble thought which he deplored: his own position was unimportant, he tried to make himself believe, compared with the jobs of more than two hundred others.

'We've got three excellent agencies looking at it now. I'm sure one of them will come up with the right answer.'

'Let's hope so, Desmond, let's hope so. And Desmond – I'm sure I don't need to say this to a man of your experience – but you must be very careful to avoid accepting any, er, hospitality from the competing agencies. You've got to be extra cautious with a major contract like this out to tender. But I'm sure you know all that without me saying so, Desmond.'

'Of course . . . sir.'

III
Luncheons

Ralph Isaacs looked down at the chessboard on the David Hicks coffee table and wondered whether to move his knight to KB3 and risk sacrificing a pawn. It was about one-thirty and much to his annoyance Jonathan Forbes, his habitual lunchtime opponent, had been temporarily dragged away to view a rough-cut commercial prior to it being shown to a client immediately after lunch. It was not a commercial in which Ralph himself had taken much interest: another formulaic toothpaste ad for Smiley – a brand which had long ago deserted Pendletons and moved to one of the many agencies which Isaacs and Isaacs had bought on their way to the top.

Ralph Isaacs, unlike any previous ad man in history, never went out to lunch. Nor to dinner. Nor to drinks. And most certainly never to parties. He rarely met any of the agency's clients, nor his competitors, nor his staff, who now numbered over six thousand around the world. This reclusive behaviour, bizarre in a business as flamboyant and gregarious as advertising, left him with a great deal of time to think, calculate and plan. He himself felt far from proud of his asceticism. He viewed himself as shy, gauche, with a volatile temper which was best kept hidden – especially from clients. Fortunately, he recognised, fate had provided him with an interpreter, a means of communication with the outside world: his cousin Stan.

Time had taught Stan how to live with Ralph's tantrums – which is not to say he enjoyed them – and now they had both reached their late thirties he gave almost as good as he got. This had been difficult for Stan to learn, as he was born a moderate, amiable, fairly placid sort, and hardly any more gregarious than Ralph. Alone together they screamed and shouted and vilified each other. Facing the outside world, they were as united and dependent on each other as medium and message.

Unlike Ralph, Stan dutifully attended business lunches on most days of the week, though they gave him little pleasure. So Ralph was surprised when his solitary lunchtime chess reverie was disturbed by his cousin entering his office.

'Bob Boyne's just phoned from Melbourne,' Stan said immediately.

'Melbourne?'

'He's over there buying another agency,' Stan explained. 'The price they're asking is exorbitant.'

'So why are they buying it?' Ralph decided that bishop to KKt5 might be a wiser move.

'Buying what?' Stan was nonplussed.

'The Melbourne agency. Anyway you said there was nothing worth buying in Melbourne. So who are they wasting money on now?'

'How should I know? I didn't think it was any of our business to ask.'

'Not our business? You need your fucking head examined, Stan. We're aiming to buy Pendletons and meanwhile they're buying some shitty shop in Melbourne and paying a ludicrously high price for it, and you say it's not any of our business? I can't believe it!' Ralph was slowly rousing himself from the calm with which chess imbued him. He poured himself some Perrier and his prehensile fingers picked up one of the tomato and watercress sandwiches that had been specially made for his lunch.

'Who said they're paying a ludicrously high price for it?'

'You did,' Ralph shouted.

'Me? How can I? I've no idea what they're paying. I don't even know who they're buying. Are you going crazy or what?'

Delicately eating his sandwich, Ralph stared down at his chessboard again, trying to recapture – despite his cousin's unbelievable stupidity – the tranquillity the ivory pieces provided. 'Listen,' he said slowly, emphasising each word, 'you burst in here, tell me Boyne's in Melbourne buying some agency which is asking an exorbitant price. Then you deny it all. Then you accuse *me* of going crazy.'

Only then did Stan spot the source of the confusion. 'It's not the price Pendletons are paying in Melbourne that's exorbitant. It's the price they want from us.'

'You mean at last they've named a price?' Ralph turned to his cousin excitedly. 'How much?'

'$600 million.'

'$600 million! For Pendletons! It's not worth half that. Not a quarter. Not a tenth. They're fucking crazy. They're living in a dream. Tell them they can stuff their shitty agency up their corporate arse. Jesus Christ! I can't believe it.'

'I told Boyne we'd consider it and get back to him.'

'We've considered it! Now leave me alone. I'm trying to play chess.'

'Where's Jonathan then?'

'Viewing some crappy Smiley rough-cut. He'll be back in a minute. $600 million! They must think we're complete schmucks.'

'It's only their first sighting shot. We'd have been suspicious if they'd started lower. Let's think about it.'

'I've thought about it. They're crazy. Their management's Byzantine, and their advertising's shit. So what are we buying for $600 million?'

'Good clients, a multinational organisation and more profits than any other agency in history. It's worth buying. But it's not worth $600 million. So we'll haggle a bit.'

'You haggle . . .'

Jonathan Forbes entered unannounced. He had worked with the Isaacs boys from the start, and they trusted him almost completely; but even he was not party to the Pendletons deal, and Ralph stopped mid-sentence.

'Got time to finish the game?' Jonathan was almost a goy replica of Ralph: both just under six foot, slim, lithe, athletic, with broad charming smiles and interested eyes. But whereas Ralph's eyes and curly hair were dark brown, Jonathan's were blue and fair; and whereas Ralph's nose was aquiline, Jonathan's was pug; and whereas Ralph was unsociable and volatile, Jonathan was sociable and imperturbable.

'If we're quick.'

'And by the way,' Stan said, deliberately annoying Ralph by picking up his last quarter of sandwich, 'Marvyn's made contact with ACM and GOB. ACM want to talk, but GOB are playing hard to get. Strange. It should be the other way round.'

'If GOB won't talk,' Ralph said as he moved his bishop, 'they've got something to hide. Has Kelly checked on Spilch Superstores yet?'

'But if they were scared of losing Spilch you'd think they'd rush to sell?'

'Not if they've lost it already. I think that'll be mate, Jonathan,' Ralph said, moving his queen unpredictably and beaming happily as he did so, his voracious competitiveness and insatiable appetite for winning momentarily assuaged by victory.

'That wasn't fair. You had hours to think while I was at the Smiley rough-cut.'

'It's never fair, Jonathan. Don't you know that by now? I always make sure I've got lots of time to think.'

'You simply wouldn't believe what happened to me this morning, It was incredible, though. Amazing.'

Hal Burton and Irving Gilbernetti were in the Vendôme listening to Trevor Kidd, the nasal Brand Manager on Crispins Squashes. Crispins Squashes was their largest remaining account, following the loss of Spilch Superstores.

'What happened, Trev?' Hal's eyes glinted with counterfeit enthusiasm.

'Well, I was coming into town off the M1, usual way down Hendon Way and through Swiss Cottage, though sometimes I turn off right before and cut through Kilburn. Do you know that way, Hal?'

Trevor Kidd, at forty-seven, was not the world's youngest Brand Manager. The three other Brand Managers at Crispins were in their twenties. The Marketing Manager at Crispins, Trevor's boss, was thirty-three. Trevor had been a marvellous salesman, not a bad Sales Manager. Then during a brief crisis in the company's history, when three Brand Managers had left simultaneously, in desperation Trevor had been drafted in to brand management. There he had contentedly stayed for some fifteen years. Each and every morning when he awoke he thanked the Lord for his success, astounded that from such humble beginnings he had risen to so high a station in life. His diligence, enthusiasm and commitment to Crispins were never in question. His kindness, helpfulness and generosity were never in doubt. As other executives came and went he provided a measure of continuity within the company. And he didn't get in anybody's way.

'I went through Swiss Cottage like a dose of salts considering it was quarter to ten, well more like ten to, to be precise. There was hardly anything on the road so I thought to myself there's something a bit fishy here. Something a bit fishy I thought—'

'Sure sounds fishy to me,' Irving interrupted effusively. 'What was it with Swiss Cottage, Trev?'

'I don't know. The road was up just before the North Circular flyover and I'd been stuck there like a goldfish in Tate and Lyle's syrup for half an hour, well twenty-five minutes anyway, so maybe that was a kind of filter. I usually think if the road's up somewhere then the next few miles after that should be a bit clearer. Have you noticed that, Hal? I'm never quite sure though. They're always mending that approach to the M1 though. Never let it alone. . . . ' Every large company has its charity employees, and Trevor was Crispins'. In times of profit drought they become savings.

'You wanna brandy or something with your coffee, Trev?'

'No thanks, Irving. Very kind of you to offer though. Never drink after lunch, that's my motto. A couple of glasses of wine or a half of bitter or a lager at midday and that's my lot. If I drink any more I go to sleep in the afternoon. Can't understand these blokes who drink all lunch-time and then they're back at their desks as if nothing had happened. Marvellous constitutions they must have. I can't do it, not by a long chalk. Not as it would matter this afternoon seeing as we've cleared all the work this morning, so I'll just be driving back up the M1. Not that I'd want to go to sleep at the wheel though, never have yet, touch wood. Have you ever gone to sleep at the wheel?'

'I sure did once, in Idaho.'

'Never have though, touch wood.'

The morning's meeting had been a good one. Hal and Irving felt mildly euphoric. They ought to get back to the agency and do some work on Splashasoap – time was passing. On the other hand Splashasoap was a bird in the bush, while Crispins was one of the few birds still in their hands. Hal considered ordering himself a port and risk being branded an alcoholic by the temperate Trev. To their surprise, Trevor had liked the new campaign they had shown him. Not that Trevor's opinion counted for a great deal at Crispins; but far better to have his friendly support than his petulant opposition.

When dealing with a company with a hierarchical multi-level structure of management, like Crispins, it is difficult to devise advertising which will be liked and approved by the many multi-level executives in the hierarchy. Such an organisational structure guarantees that no advertising which is wayward, unusual, truly striking or completely original will ever appear; equally it guarantees that advertising which is too foolish or off-the-track will not appear either. When producing new campaigns for such clients Hal and Irving, like all good admen, first assessed which of the multi-executives was the most powerful and cared most about the advertising. It was rarely the top man. (To most top businessmen advertising is a small pimple which rises from time to time and if dealt with sensibly goes away.) At Crispins the key man happened to be Trevor's boss, and the new ads had been planned and designed with his views and prejudices much in mind. To have won Trevor's support was a desirable bonus.

'I drove straight into Regent's Park, turning left at the Outer Circle like I always do because then I can drive down past the Nash Terraces where there's never any room because it gets full up with the early commuters. If you want to park by those Nash Terraces I should think you'd need to be there by eight thirty at the latest, eight o'clock I shouldn't wonder. Very nice place to park though. But I've got my spot, you know where Hal, in that mews behind York Gate and though it says Private I've been parking there for years. I reckon they know my car by now though. They probably say, "That's old Trevor Kidd's car", I shouldn't wonder and leave it at that.' This happy thought made Trevor smile. Hal and Irving grinned supportively.

'So what's happened, Trev?' Irving asked, as breathless as he could manage.

'That's it. That's the point though. I'd never have believed my eyes. In all my born days I've never been so surprised.'

'The plot sickens.'

'Instead of just this white board saying Private, lettered in Times Roman I should think, though I've never been quite certain. Have you ever seen that notice, Hal? The serifs look a bit heavy for Times Roman to me. There was this bar up.'

'What bar?'

'That was it. Couldn't get into the mews at all. The blighters have put this bar up.'

'Jesus!' Irving whistled lightly through his teeth. 'Jesus, Trev! So the game was up! Zam, kepow, and you're out. 'What did you do then Trev?'

'Sure you won't have a brandy, Trevor?'

'No thanks, Hal. Very kind of you to offer though. What could I do? What would you do? I backed out from the mews which was very tight and I didn't want a scraper, not just then I didn't. I drove round Regent's Park looking for a spot to park, it being ten past ten by then or maybe it was only five past and sometimes a few early parkers are moving off by then. I nearly got one too, round by the Baker Street gate, but a blue mini got there just a split second before me, or maybe it was two or three seconds.'

'Boy, have you sure had a morning, Trev.'

'Then, when I really thought I'd had my chips and it was all over and I thought I'd have to park in the bloody Hilton and pay their bloody prices after all, and I was thinking What about the future? Where am I going to park in the future? I can't keep putting in expense chitties for parking at the Hilton, not at their prices I can't. They'll end up by making me come down by train. You can imagine how I was feeling though. Well, you're like me, Hal, hate wasting money I know, and I was just going to drive out of the park by Great Portland Street and bless my luck if a blooming great Buick which was parked there doesn't pull out and I just managed to slip in quick, though there was this old green Cortina which nearly beat me to it, the blighter. You have to be so quick in London, it's like the blooming dodgems. The quick and the dead. Anyway I got in before him. P registration I think he was, so he wouldn't have had the acceleration as he had to do a hundred yards in three seconds I should think. Not a second more.'

Hal and Irving, sensing that the climax of Trevor's morning drama had been passed, relaxed. It was quarter to three. Well, maybe nearer ten to. Hal called for the bill. His Sole Cubat had been a little overcooked, but the Brie for a change had been perfect, and he could have done with a little more. Trevor had professed to enjoy his prawn cocktail, medium fillet steak and Cheddar as effusively as he always did. The Vendôme wasn't what it used to be in the good old days of Mr Walsh, Hal thought, but then there was nowhere decent in London any more that wasn't grossly overpriced.

'And then,' Trevor started again, his brilliantined hair immaculately tidy, his Marks and Spencer's suit, shirt and tie sensibly unprovocative, staring fixedly ahead as though hypnotised by a fly on the restaurant wall, 'just as I was locking up safe and sound and thinking to myself what a stroke of luck at the eleventh hour and what should I see? You wouldn't believe it! A blooming traffic warden walking towards my car and sticking fines on every single blighter parked there! We were *all* parked illegally. That's why the Buick left in such a blooming hurry, I shouldn't wonder. Knew she was coming I dare say. So—'

'Jesus, Trev. I can't take it. Please let us out of our misery, Trev. Let us off the hook. Did you park in the Hilton or not? In the end, I mean, after the traffic warden and everything?'

'Well what do you think? What could I do? I went to the Hilton and it was full. So I parked at that one at Shepherd's Market. Very reasonable it is. Do you know it, Hal?'

Until that moment it had never occurred to Chris Beaumont that Desmond Digby was rather handsome, but as soon as the ageing Gary Cable entered the restaurant, to much bowing and scraping from the normally arrogant and contemptuous waiters, Chris noticed a striking resemblance. Cable, one of Hollywood's greatest stars, though now well into his seventies, doubtless kept his hair and trim moustache jet black with the Californian equivalent of Grecian 2000; his dentition appeared unchanged since his great romantic roles of the forties and fifties; his lightly tanned skin was – apart from the famous laughter lines around his mouth and eyes – almost unwrinkled. (Chris wondered whether it was now normal in Beverley Hills for men, too, to have face-lifts.) Altogether he was in excellent shape, and looked about thirty years younger than he was.

Chris had never before taken Des Digby to lunch, an omission he was now regretting. Des clearly enjoyed being entertained expensively. It was the flattering implication that he was a person of power and importance – rather than the food or the wine – that Des obviously found gratifying. To be taken to lunch by the Chairman of Pendletons, and in a restaurant populated by other Chairmen and by movie stars, compared very favourably with being taken to dinner at the Casa Roma by Hal Burton. Des Digby would indubitably tell his wife that evening (and everyone at the golf club at the weekend) about lunching in the same restaurant as Gary Cable. It was a pity, he reflected, that Chris had waited three years and had only been nudged into it by the threat of losing Splashasoap.

They were sitting in London's most expensive restaurant, named La Brioche with typically modest Gallic understatement. The name, it was apparently hoped, would somehow charm the sting out of the exorbitant prices. *Nouvelle cuisine*, Chris thought, was one of the finer confidence tricks ever perpetrated by the catering industry. His own *Feuillantine d'ailes de cailles 'truffées' de cèpes* had been overcooked and tasted squidgy, but Des had seemed to like his *Carré D'Agneau Rôti au Four Parfumé au Romarin*, and had undoubtedly relished the Château Ducru Beaucaillou 1975 – with his eyes, even if not with his palate. Having ordered his first kir royal almost before he had sat down, and followed it with two more in quick succession, Des had clearly arrived at La Brioche determined to enjoy himself.

Gluttony apart, it had not been an easy lunch. Des had, as he had announced he would after his first kir royal, 'spoken his mind, because that was the way he liked to deal with people,

straight from the shoulder with no beating around the bush.'
'I'd really appreciate that,' Chris concurred, 'that's the way we at Pendletons always like to deal with our clients. Getting problems out into the open, no holds barred. Only way to solve them I think.'

'Right,' said Des, and promptly launched into a flood of spiteful and – in Chris's view – largely unjustified invective against Flora Thompson and Francis Kemp-Lewis, with the Vicar taking the brunt of the attack. Flora, Des damned her with faint praise, was terribly bright, no doubt about it, but a bit too academic for the cut and thrust of toilet soap marketing, a bit too toffee-nosed (that was only his opinion, mind you, and he knew he could be wrong) to understand C2 housewives in Sheffield. Not – Des added quickly, sensing that his criticisms were upsetting Chris – that he was asking for her to be taken off the Splashasoap account, far from it, he greatly valued her clarity of thinking. (Clients like Des Digby grumble incessantly but rarely wield a knife, thought Chris). No, Larsons needed people with Flora's intelligence and objectivity on their business most definitely but perhaps she needed stronger back-up, maybe somebody heavier than Simon Booth, who seemed a little lightweight; perhaps it was just his youth, perhaps somebody with more experience of the cut and thrust of toiletry marketing, experienced at the coalface so to speak. . . .

Suddenly it clicked. Chris perceived why they were in such trouble with Larsons, why Splashasoap was at risk. Pendletons had committed the cardinal advertising agency sin of not providing a friend for the client. Des Digby respected Flora and acknowledged, albeit grudgingly, that she did a good job on the Larsons' account. But he didn't feel comfortable with her, didn't view her as a mate with whom he could down a few drinks or go out on the town. Yes, Splashasoap's sales were below target, and doubtless Des was under pressure from Peter Dalrymple; and doubtless Dalrymple himself was under pressure from his Chairman. But if Des had had a chum at Pendletons, a chum with whom he could have had a straight-from-the-shoulder-no-beating-about-the-bush conversation – after a few large G and Ts or kir royals – then the possible impending disaster could easily have been averted, the sword of Damocles would not now be dangling above Pendletons' head. That was why Des was now asking for somebody older and more experienced than Simon: he wanted an agency chum – though he himself probably did not even realise it.

Chris cursed himself once again for not having entertained Des Digby previously. Sins of omission always return to thump you on the nose. Though, he excused himself guiltily to himself, he lunched and dined with clients and prospective clients most days and, well, most nights; and Digby was quite junior at Larsons. Flora should have been able to cope with him. If she couldn't she should have mentioned it – but Chris knew that to be a pipe-dream: nobody in an agency ever admits they cannot get on with a major client, because to do so is career suicide. No, it was Chris's job to perceive the easily perceivable likelihood that ex-Cheltenham Ladies College and Girton Flora Thompson was an improbable soulmate for Des Digby. That, Chris knew as he cut at his quails and tried to disentangle a few mouthfuls of meat, was his own cock-up and there was no baulking it. His judgment had been impaired.

Digby's criticisms of Francis Kemp-Lewis were more predictable, and simultaneously both more and less perturbing. Less perturbing because Chris had heard them from other clients before, and because he now knew they were not the root cause of the Larsons' problem; but more perturbing because they spotlit a fundamental long-term management dilemma to which Chris had not yet found a solution: how to replace Kemp-Lewis with somebody who was a better creative director but equally acceptable to those Pendletons clients – including the mammoth Marmaduke Confectionery – who were committed, and intended to remain committed, to the 3-S philosophy, the more abstruse implications of which (difficult though this may be to believe) Francis could and often did discuss with Jesuitical fervour.

'The trouble with the old Vicar,' Des Digby, like everyone else, used his nickname, 'is he hasn't got the creative spark any more. I mean, correct me if I'm wrong, but those youngsters – Tom Nathan and that Irish boy, I've forgotten his name – well, you've got to be young to keep coming up with fresh ideas in

your business, or that's the way it seems to me, anyway. . . . '
Des Digby deemed his slightly deferential tone appropriate for conversations with the Chairman of his agency. Nobody else at Pendletons ever heard him say 'correct me if I'm wrong.'

Unaware of this, Chris noted and took comfort from Des's enthusiasm for Nathan and O'Reilly. Thank goodness he had accepted – subject to research of course – the Smashin' campaign. It would be essential for the two youngsters to present their idea themselves at the final pitch. He would need tactfully to persuade the Vicar – whose job it would normally be – to stand down and let the boys do it.

'Yes, an armagnac would be very acceptable. . . . ' Des Digby was addressing the sommelier who was standing by the table displaying a trolley laden with immodestly priced vintage cognacs, armagnacs, ports and liqueurs when the hubbub broke out at the door of the restaurant.

Television news, it transpired, had discovered the presence of Gary Cable at La Brioche and the cameras were waiting on the pavement upstairs to film his departure. The management of La Brioche affected to find this intrusion on the privacy of their clientele exceedingly disagreeable, though their irritation may possibly have been assuaged by the knowledge that it could do the restaurant's already buoyant trade no harm for megastar Gary Cable to be seen leaving. Cable's reaction seemed to be to let the television paparazzi wait: he was in no hurry to leave.

Chris Beaumont, in contrast, was in a great hurry to leave. He had just noticed that it was after three o'clock, which meant he would be late, again, for an important meeting with the Marketing Director of Marmaduke. Fortunately his chauffeur was outside, waiting to whisk him to Milton Keynes, but he would never get there by four o'clock. 'Gosh,' he said to Des, not wishing to imply that he had other clients more important than Larsons but nonetheless keen to depart, 'I've just noticed how late it is. I really must get going. Waiter, waiter, the bill. . . . '

To Chris's surprise, Des Digby reacted to this news with consternation. Remembering Peter Dalrymple's admonition, he did not wish to be filmed leaving London's plushest eaterie with (or even without) Chris Beaumont. Though the TV cameras were there to film Gary Cable, they might easily decide to film, and to transmit, a few shots of other customers to add colour. He would have preferred not to have needed to explain all that to Chris Beaumont, but saw little alternative as Beaumont had already stood up to leave. 'Look,' he said, desperately adjusting the truth a trifle, 'it wouldn't be right for the other agencies pitching for our account to see me leaving La Brioche with you. If we get filmed, I mean . . . they might feel they had to bring me here too!' He laughed unconvincingly. 'I don't want to eat here every day! Can you ask if there's a back entrance for the staff, or something. I really don't want to be filmed leaving.'

The chap must be cracked, thought Chris, or drunker than he seemed. Still, this was no time to annoy him, and he was palpably agitated.

'*Certainement*, Monsieur Beaumont,' the manager responded to his request as he led them through the Louis Quatorze furniture and out through the immaculate Delft-tiled kitchens, 'you can walk along *le passage* under the railings and climb the stairs into Curzon Street in about *cent mètres*.'

'Thanks, Chris.' Desmond sounded surprisingly sincere as they walked along the damp basement passageway. 'I won't forget this.'

It would be ironic, Chris thought, as they climbed the wrought-iron stairs into the street, if he had succeeded in holding on to the Larsons' account by spiriting Des Digby out of the staff entrance of La Brioche. Emerging on to the pavement he looked back to the restaurant's main entrance, spotted his chauffeur and thoughtlessly shouted to him.

Some of the TV crew turned. They spotted Des Digby looking, at over a hundred yards' distance, more than a little like Gary Cable (whom anyway none of them had seen since his last screen appearance in *Midnight in Athens* eighteen years previously). 'That's him,' one of them yelled 'he's trying to escape,' whereupon they all gave chase, tearing down Curzon Street trailing wires and bits of recording equipment, with the cameraman huffing, puffing and trying to hold the view-finder to his eyes as he ran.

Seeing them rushing towards him Des Digby turned on his

heels and scampered off under the arch into Shepherd's Market, his briefcase flailing, and as he shoved out of his way two street-walkers plying for afternoon hire one of them bellowed, 'You cunt!' at his rapidly retreating posterior.

You've got to hand it to Mike Coventry, Harry Adams thought as he cut himself some Dolcelatte and spread it delicately on to a hunk of baguette, he's a great planner, when he gets his finger out. London's best. It had been a smart move setting up with Bill and Mike: the best creative man and the best account planner in town. Yoked together with his own commercial acumen they were, he congratulated himself, an unbeatable team.

They were having a working lunch in their office, under the £23,700 sculptured ceiling, and Mike Coventry was presenting to his two partners his analysis of the Splashasoap problem, interrupting himself occasionally to eat his portion of mushroom quiche or take a swig from his Budweiser can. The pale, veneered table which they used as a shared desk was laden with two kinds of pâté; a large mushroom quiche; a plate of Parma ham, bresaola, mortadella and salami; a cheese board with Brie, Camembert, Stilton, Cheddar and Dolcelatte; a basket which originally contained three small baguettes; a plate of mixed biscuits for the cheese; butter; a fruit bowl overflowing with apples, oranges, pears, grapes, bananas and plums; a dozen cans of Budweiser; three unused glasses; and as yet unused coffee cups and saucers. Sufficient to feed a small army – or an average-sized commercial film crew – most of which would be left uneaten by Messrs Adams, Coventry and McAndrew and consumed by the agency's secretaries, as one of their rightful perks, during the course of the afternoon. Bill McAndrew, perturbed by the un-kosher nature of the repast, ate only an apple and a few grapes.

'Ast . . . astonishing though it sounds, est . . . est . . . estimates of the toilet soap market vary widely' Mike Coventry's stammer was playing him up, as he placed a transparency on the overhead projector. On the built-in screen which dropped down magically from the sculptured ceiling at the press of a remote-control button was displayed:

TOILET SOAP MARKET
ESTIMATED SIZE:
£89,000,000 at RSP
Source: Data Quest

'...b...b... because there is a sub... stantial market for non-domestic toilet soaps, at w... work and in leisure establishments, of un... un... unknown size, and of course there is subs... stantial price-cutting at retail. Anyway £89 million s... s... seems the best sterling estimate available, and everyone agrees that volumes have been static at around s... s... sixty-five thousand tonnes for years now.'

He downed a long gulp of Budweiser hoping it would relieve his stammer, which came and went, and it helped. Putting another transparency on to the projector he continued: 'Everyone also agrees that liquid soaps like Splashasoap are about three per cent of the total, with maximum, abs... abs... absolutely maximum, sales of £3 million, including Marks and Sparks, and so Splashasoap, although it's brand leader with about two-thirds of the business, can't be selling more than £2 million at retail selling prices, t... top whack, or £1.4 million to Larsons.'

'But that's what they've been spending on advertising,' Harry cut in. He hadn't analysed the market, but he knew what was in it for the agency.

'Y... y... yes. It seems extraordinary to me, too. B... b... but the explanation is that in America the liquid soap market is b... b... booming. And Larsons are obviously investing against it happening here. They c... can't break into the soap market head-on against Levers, Procter and Colgate, because they're not b... b... big enough. But if they can establish Splashasoap b... b... before liquid soaps take off here, they'll be in a s... s... strong position when the day comes.'

'Och, meanwhile they're losing their shirts.' One of Bill McAndrews rare strengths as an advertising creative man was that – despite Harry Adams' views to the contrary – he took a considerable interest in, and was fascinated by, marketing data.

'T . . . . t . . . they can afford it. If they want to. And the g . . . good thing from our point of view is they're obviously c . . . c . . . committed for the long term.'

Tall, thin and gangly with a small head perched apparently precariously on his adams-appled neck, wearing rimless spectacles and rarely smiling, Mike Coventry was indeed, as Harry Adams knew, at only thirty-three, reputed to be the best account planner in London. Account planning, a new and arcane advertising discipline which originated either at J. Walter Thompson or at Boase, Massimi, Pollitt (both laid claim to its invention), had become the fashionably acceptable face of market research in the new-wave agencies in London – though it was little known, and less understood, in the rest of the world. Most people, and especially most account planners, found it difficult to define. But Mike Coventry was clear and characteristically precise: 'Account planning at ACM' (as he said on the agency's excellent promotional videotape) 'is the interface between the market-place and the creative department. It is the collection and analysis of data on the basis on which we hammer out creative objectives and strategies and then, through research, check that we have successfully communicated the message we intended to.' (Much to his relief, and after a nerve-racking start, he took the fifth take without a stammer.)

'At the m . . . m . . . moment,' he went on as one of the secretaries brought in coffee and began to clear the uneaten victuals from the table, 'research shows that twenty-one per cent of women use liquid soap . . . ' he put another transparency on the projector which displayed the demographic profile of liquid soap users ' . . . and not s . . . s . . . surprisingly, they tend to be ABC1 in social class, living in L . . . London and in the south east, at work, b . . . but surprisingly old, to me at least, m . . . m . . . mostly aged thirty-five to fifty-four.'

'That is odd,' agreed Harry, 'usually new trends like liquid soaps are taken up by the young, and the middle-aged follow suit later. What's the explanation, Mike? Hey, don't take away the cheese yet,' he restrained an over-zealous (or perhaps hungry) secretary.

'It's d . . . difficult to be certain, b . . . b . . . but it's certainly odd. And it d...d...doesn't bode well for the f...f... future of the market, on which Larsons are p...pinning their hopes.' Mike was clearly growing excited by the problem, and it was exacerbating his stammer; he took a long draught of beer. 'It's maybe that younger women don't find the idea appealing but I...I...don't think that makes sense. No. My theory is,' and suddenly his stammer disappeared, 'that the pack is old fashioned. Look at it.' He picked the Splashasoap pack up from the table and waved it at them. 'Typical downmarket housewifey design, guaranteed to put off the younger consumers. But more importantly, the advertising is typical Pendletons' rubbish, 3-S at its worst: "Gunge and grime go away when you use Splashasoap every day".'

He switched on the videoplayer and the three of them watched an embarrassingly gauche two Cs in a K commercial, and broke into uproarious laughter.

'What crap,' Bill McAndrew said through his giggles, 'I thought ads like that had gone out with the ark.'

'Y...you never watch telly, Bill, or you'd see lots like that every n...n...night. Anyway that's my strategy. We've got to re-package Splashasoap completely and promote it to the young. W...w...what do you think?'

'Great,' Bill said immediately. 'Great. That's something we can get our teeth into. I like it. Mike, you're a genius.'

'Not bad. Not bad at all.' Harry condescendingly added his congratulations, taking off his scarlet-framed specs, foreseeing another sackful of lucre entering the agency's electronically operated portals.

Not even its most devoted regulars believed The Quills to be the loveliest pub in London. Situated in North Soho, just off Charlotte Street, in the slightly seedy area which its residents – seeking to make a faster buck from their freeholds – have dubbed fashionable Fitzrovia, The Quills had somehow successfully sidestepped the brewers' red-plush-and-horse-brasses-seventies-smartening-up which most West End pubs have suffered. It had never served a single scampi-in-a-basket or chilli con carne in all its years, determinedly providing its customers with a choice of giant bangers or drying cheese rolls on a take 'em or leave 'em basis. Wally and Molly, the landlord and his missus, had been in charge since shortly after Wally's demob in 1946 and it was widely believed, by Wally and Molly along with everyone else, that the brewery was awaiting Wally's demise – which in view of his girth, chain smoking, and cholesterol level was unlikely to involve too protracted a delay – before sending in what Wally called 'the tight-arsed little nancy brigade' to bring in the red plush and chilli con carne or even, worse still, to turn it into a wine bar.

At which point Tom Nathan, Paul O'Reilly and all the other advertising creative folk who adored The Quills and abhorred microwave pub food would doubtless desert the grubby old place and seek pastures new, or rather old, again. Quite why so many of those in sunrise, hi-tech communications industries are enamoured by sunset, low-tech, spit and sawdust nooks and crannies is a riddle wrapped in an enigma.

'Another pint please, Wal,' called Tom, 'and two Pils, a white wine, a red and a Perrier.'

It was twenty-five past two. Tom Nathan was on his sixth pint, Paul O'Reilly on his fifth Pils, and they were with 'Baby' Jane Ryman and Roy Clough, one of the best creative teams at DDB ('which ain't saying much these days,' Tom normally added when Jane and Roy weren't present), and Johnny Heist. Johnny, the oldest copywriter still practising, and still winning creative awards, who had changed jobs as often as Procter and Gamble rejected storyboards, was currently employed at Isaacs and Isaacs. Although all their lunch-breaks officially ended at two, none of them displayed the slightest inclination to quit the pub.

'Fred called me this morning,' Roy was saying, 'wanted to know if Jane and me would move to Davidson Pearce. Big ackers. But I'm not sure where they're going right now. They've not done anything good since Colt.' Roy peered through his thick lenses and grinned cheekily. 'Unless you fancy fucking chimps of course. Did you know all the PG chimps are girls, and cause big problems when they're on heat? No good to me though. I'm a sheep man myself.'

'What about International Wool? And P&O? I think Davidson Pearce are real good . . . I think we should really think about it.' 'Baby' Jane, Roy's art director, was so called because she weighed nearly thirteen stone and was often affectionately described as the fattest lady in advertising.

'Go on your own if you like. I'm not leaving DDB. We've only been there seven months. Maybe it's not been great, but it's getting better.' Roy was adamant.

'No chance, love,' Johnny Heist offered them the benefit of his not inconsiderable experience. 'When I worked there in the 1960s it was the hottest shop in town. In the world. You know what I mean? When Bill Bernbach died the light went out, love.' Johnny, who at sixty-two did weight training, bleached his hair blond, never drank or smoked and looked younger than everyone present, though they were half his age, had always (if he were to be believed) worked at agencies when they were at their creative zenith.

'I think Davidson Pearce is a real good agency,' 'Baby' Jane repeated.

'Their art direction's not so strong though. Not these days.' Paul O'Reilly pensively sipped his Pils.

'Better than fucking Pendletons,' Roy laughed.

'Everywhere's better than Pendletons,' Jane confirmed.

'Pendletons ain't so bad, but still . . . ' Tom Nathan hated being forced to defend his choice of employers, but frequently found himself doing so when among London's advertising *glitterati*. Among advertising creative people there is a hierarchy of agencies. It isn't published anywhere, but everyone knows it. There might be, indeed there repeatedly are, ferocious arguments about the exact placings of agencies on the list – 'GGT are more creative than BBH!' 'WCRS is less creative than BMP!' – but its broad structure is broadly agreed upon. And Pendletons was a long way from the top.

'Well I'd never work there, love,' Johnny Heist said, glancing surreptitiously in The Quill's peeling bar mirror and then straightening his curly hair, 'but then they couldn't afford me.' Johnny watched himself laugh in the mirror, admired his thirty-two uncrowned teeth, worried about his wrinkles forming around his eyes, and continued, 'Ralph and Stan aren't as black as they're painted. You know what I mean? Not if you're creative. And they know I'm creative.'

Everyone in town, Tom thought, knows Johnny's creative, because he never tires of saying so: also, he's creative.

'If you won't go to Davidson Pearce,' Tom asked, 'where would you go?'

'Don't know. Adams Coventry maybe. They're doing fantastic work.'

'Everyone says it's a real nasty place to work,' said 'Baby' Jane, 'a real nasty sweat shop. Anyone want another drink?'

It was five to three. Wally was calling last orders and washing glasses on his antiquated glasswasher. Johnny dragged his eyes from the mirror, finished his Perrier and announced that he had to get back early as he had a lot of work on.

'Funny you mentioning ACM,' Tom said to Roy as they left the pub. 'Fred phoned yesterday and asked if Paul and I were interested. They told 'er they're pitching for a big new account they're sure they're gonna win. But they won't pay more than we're getting now. So we can't see the point in it, but still.'

'I told you it was a real sweat shop. It really is.'

'It's a million times better than fucking Pendletons.'

'I wonder,' Tom Nathan rhetorically and somewhat inebriatedly asked Paul as they strolled back to Pendletons through the littered streets, 'whether advertising people ever talk about anything except advertising. Or even think about anything except advertising?'

They passed a wire newspaper display rack laden with newspapers announcing the latest hijack massacre, scattered among a miscellany of porn magazines on the covers of which girls with massive mammaries were bent into every shape and contortion that the minds of lascivious photographers could devise.

'And sex, I'm thinking,' Paul answered Tom's rhetorical question, while thoughtfully kicking a polystyrene Big Mac container into the gutter.

IV
Liaisons

'... and in Belfast, in another sectarian killing, a father and his nine-year-old daughter were shot dead when masked gunmen entered their living room.

'... Finally, in Nicosia the three Arab gunmen who hijacked the Pan Am 747 in Karachi and killed thirty-one of the passengers during the attempt to storm the plane last night were today being questioned by Cypriot authorities. The PLO has denied any responsibility for the hijacking and so far it has not been possible to identify the terrorist group to which the gunmen belong. In addition to the thirty-one dead, ninety-six of the Pan Am passengers are still in hospital, thirteen of them in a critical condition....'

'Please switch off,' Jenny Sandford asked Simon Booth, who was lying, still nude, on her small settee and fiddling with the television remote-control unit.

'In a sec. I just want to see the ads. There should be one of ours in this break.'

On Dave Horrell's weekly memo, which notified all agency staff of the times when Pendletons' commercials were to be transmitted, there was a Pierre Renoir commercial scheduled to follow *News at Ten*. Pierre Renoir Perfumes was Simon's other client, and although it was far smaller in the UK than Larsons it was one of Pendletons' major multinational accounts, annually spending $30 million around the globe. Hence Pendletons' American top management took a close interest in its well-being. Its owner, a lady from the Bronx named Gertie Tannenbaum, was notoriously demanding and ill-tempered, with a penchant for changing her ad agency every two or three years because, as she was quoted in *Advertising Age* as saying: 'You advertising jerks are complacent, martini-drinking bums who'd take a five-hour lunch-hour and spend all the rest of your time pinning creative awards on each other's chests if you had the chance. Well you ain't taking Gertie Tannenbaum's business for granted.'

Pendletons having held the account for two-and-a-half years fissures were starting to appear, since Ms Tannenbaum's staff around the world were well aware of her views and knew that after two years (at the most) they would be expected to start carping about the agency's performance. She liked them to make lists of the agency's misdemeanours, however trivial, and to send them to her as soon as they reached 'unlucky thirteen'. In the honeymoon period following each new agency's appointment it might take twelve months for a local manager to reach the required baker's dozen. But by the third year new lists piled on to her desk with every post, from every country where Pierre Renoir Perfumes were advertised. Thus her expressed convictions were irrefutably confirmed, and she could not comprehend why otherwise smart companies like General Motors and Coca Cola stayed with the same advertising agencies indefinitely; but then, as she so often raucously proclaimed, the perfume business ain't like no other business.

Currently her UK manager was grumbling about the sound level of the voice-over which Pendletons had dubbed on to an American commercial. It was so quiet, he claimed, you needed a deaf-aid to hear the words. Simon had been assured that the commercial's decibel level was normal, and had passed on this assurance to his client, who remained unconvinced. Hence Simon was anxious to hear the commercial on air for himself. All of which he had explained to Jenny, who had not been notably sympathetic.

Having made herself some tea, which Simon had rejected, Jenny sat down in her bentwood rocking chair, in her Marks and Spencer towelling dressing gown, and gazed affectionately around her tiny flatlet while Simon stared intently at the TV screen. It was the first dwelling in which she had ever lived completely alone, the first she had ever felt to be her own. The reproduction Magritte, the junior gymkhana red rosettes she had won on Mr Plod, the three-spotlight standard lamp illuminating her books on the shelf, were all surveyed by Wellington, her adored and now retired-from-active-service teddy, sitting in his recently purchased Victorian high-chair. She rented the flat furnished, and the furniture was dowdy and a bit worn; but to Jenny it had quickly become home.

'... all over the world', the advertising break had started, 'Pan Am. You can't beat the experience.' And the celestial singers rounded off the commercial with the rising and rousing jingle 'Pa... a... an... Am'.

Jenny's clandestine relationship with Simon was entering its sixth month; in August they had even sneaked a week's holiday in a borrowed caravan in the Loire Valley without anyone at Pendletons suspecting. Being in different departments helped; as an invoice clerk she had no reason to make contact with Simon during the day, and they rarely even passed each other in the corridors. Occasionally she suspected Simon was so insistent on secrecy because he was ashamed of her: she was well aware that she was neither physically nor socially the type of girl to whom old-Harrovian Oxford graduates aspire. But she herself had no desire to go public: from the start she had known that it would end – the possibility of marriage was never in question – and she had no wish to be the object first of gossip, then of pity.

'Sshhh. . . . ' Simon exclaimed unnecessarily as a voice sounding not quite like Maurice Chevalier intoned against a rendition of *La Mer* sounding not quite like Henry Mancini: 'Every woman knows those secret moments . . . those moments of joy . . . of bliss . . . of mystery . . . those moments when only the warmest, subtlest fragrance will . . . how do you say in Engleeesh? . . . reflect her most beautiful self. Those moments are . . . for Pierre Renoir. Pierre Renoir . . . for moments of joy . . . of bliss . . . of mystery . . .'

Although she could not see the screen Jenny knew the commercial well: opening on an aerial shot of the Château de Chenonceaux – their caravan site had been less than thirty kilometres away – the camera moved inside to follow a gossamer apparition of a model wistfully climbing a massive marble staircase, entering a huge bedroom, glancing momentarily at herself in a luxuriously ornate dressing-table mirror, and draping herself elegantly on an emperor size four-poster bed, while almost instantaneously a young officer looking not quite like Gérard Philippe appeared, kissed her lightly on the lips and the image faded into . . . a Pierre Renoir pack.

'That's loud enough,' Simon almost bellowed, 'quite loud enough!' Heard every word, no trouble. Deaf-aid! It was loud enough, wasn't it, Jen?'

'It wasn't all that loud. But I didn't think it was meant to be.'

'Balls! Sorry.' On those rare occasions when Simon swore in front of girls, he always felt immediately and uncomfortably guilty.

'Well, I don't really like the advert anyway.'

'Nor do I,' Simon agreed enthusiastically, 'it's rubbish. Typical American rubbish. They make us use it. You should hear what Tom Nathan says about it.'

'What does he say?'

'I . . . I couldn't repeat his language. Anyway I can't stand the bloke.'

Jenny looked at Simon's pale freckly body. There was still a residual swimming trunk tan line across his stomach and hips; he was so long and skinny he looked like a scarecrow. Whereas she herself was short, broad shouldered and stocky, with thick legs and big hips, accompanied unfairly (she had always felt) by boyishly small boobs. Fortunately, she consoled herself, certain men found her long flame-red tresses irresistible; and Simon, as he frequently told her, was one of them.

'Anyway I've thought of a way to get my own back on him.' Simon often tended to talk in terms reminiscent of Biggles.

'Oh?' Jenny sounded surprised. Vindictiveness and revenge were not normally Simon's style.

'They've asked me to set up the research to test his new Splashasoap campaign. I'm seeing Greg Hamilton about it tomorrow. On my own,' he added proudly. Greg Hamilton was a name to conjure with. Irritatingly Jenny had patently never heard of him.

'So?'

'I've thought of a way to bend the research. Nobody will spot it. I'll tell Greg Hamilton to do the research among women who are hostile to using liquid soaps. I'll say it's because we want to expand the market by winning them over.'

'So?'

'If they're against the product it's jolly well certain they'll be against the commercial. It always works like that. If you don't like the product you don't like the ads. So they'll reject smart-arse Nathan's creativity hook, line and sinker.'

Jenny was silent for a few moments. She disliked Simon trying to be devious and tough, and she noticed that the excitement of his plot seemed to be arousing him.

'Won't that be . . .' she searched for the phrase, and heard herself sound like her mum, ' . . . be cutting off your nose to spite your face? If Pendletons lose Splashasoap, I mean.'

'Course not. We're already working on other campaigns. One of the other teams is bound to come up with something a jolly sight better. Larsons would have given Nathan and O'Reilly's lousy effort the thumbs down anyway. If we present their stuff we're bound to lose the business. It's all wrong, from the client's POV. So the sooner I kill it off the better.'

Jenny noticed Simon's slim, carefully manicured hand stray, unconsciously, down towards his groin.

'Here,' he whispered. 'Come over here.'

'I think I'll have a bath,' she replied. They had already made love once that evening and it hadn't been great.

'. . . to which the gunmen belong. In addition to the thirty-one dead, thirty-six of the Pan Am passengers are still in hospital, thirteen of them in a critical condition. . . . '

'Do switch off, darling,' Flora Thompson asked Chris Beaumont, who was lying in his Viyella paisley dressing-gown, on her buttoned leather chesterfield, with his head in her lap.

'In a sec. We ought to watch the break. I think there's one of ours. The Pierre Renoir job the client's being playing up about.' Chris Beaumont frequently suffered little twinges of guilt because he so rarely watched television, particularly commercial television. It was, he knew, the duty of every diligent adman to watch the commercials in order to keep up with the latest trends and happenings; though, as he also knew, few top admen have either the time or the inclination to do so. In his own case he felt the requirement to be particularly pressing as he still felt himself to be slightly out of touch, having run Pendletons' Milan office before returning to run London.

'You know Pierre Renoir are just looking for trouble. They want to fire us, and any excuse will do.' Flora Thompson expounded the view that had become conventional wisdom in the agency. When a client becomes perpetually pernickety everyone knows the agency is on the skids.

'I don't want to give them any more excuses than I have to. It will all get back to Boyne. And when the global chopper finally falls the Americans are bound to blame everyone but themselves. They'll edit Gertie Tannenbaum's little lists to prove that it was all our fault, and that they were whiter than white. And I'll get another of those lovely Boyne telexes chewing my balls off. Hang on, this is it.'

'... Those moments are for Pierre Renoir. Pierre Renoir ... moments of joy ... of bliss ... of mystery ...'

'Not bad. For one of ours. Marvellous shot of Chenonceaux against the sunlight. I wonder how they did it,' Flora said, running her fingers affectionately through her lover's grey wavy hair.

He flicked off the television with the remote control. 'Cost a fortune. Well over $600,000. They intended using it all over the world. Now Gertie's gone off it, so she's refusing to pay.'

'What a bitch she must be.' Flora's voice contained a tiny hint of admiration.

'Just a typical American client. American clients treat their agencies like shit. You've no idea how lucky we are in this country. You've never worked abroad.'

After leaving Cambridge, Flora Thompson had joined Young and Rubicam as a graduate trainee, and had stayed there for nine happy years, rising steadily through the ranks, until she married the Deputy Creative Director and left to avoid the problems which (everybody said) would ensue from having a married couple working in the same agency. She moved to Pendletons and stayed put, as much as anything because the break-up of her marriage – he had taken to drink and grown violent when passed over for the Creative Directorship twice running – had been protracted and painful. She had needed the steady, stormless working environment that Pendletons had provided through those tempestuous years.

Now, at thirty-seven, she felt no desire to remarry, nor to have children; and she generally avoided thinking about the future.

Her affair with Chris Beaumont was just over a year old; they had celebrated their first anniversary with dinner at Le Brioche, but only after Chris, taking advantage of his status as a regular and respected customer, had checked the name of every other diner who had reserved a table that evening. It did not infallibly guarantee none of the other diners would know them; but as Chris said, it lessened the odds.

Very occasionally they drove out to a tiny pub which Chris knew, near Egham, but it was a horrid drive; and twice they had engineered business trips together. Otherwise, and mostly, they spent two or three evenings each week together at her flat, before he returned home to his wife and immaculate Georgian house in Kensington. (She had inspected it, indeed snooped all around it, when he had been on holiday.) His house, which looked so majestic and mature, made her feel more than ever uncomfortable about her Maida Vale flat, and as she looked around her she knew why. Everything in it was too young for her. The pop colours, the art gallery advertisements, the floor cushions, the canvas directors' chairs, the planted Casa Fina birdcage, the brightly coloured felt parrot swinging on his perch: they were all fine for people in their twenties but she felt more and more ill at ease with them, as though she were wearing clothes of the wrong age for her. The problem was that she did not know how, in furnishing terms, to dress her age: her tastes had not advanced with her years. Only the recently acquired chesterfield now fitted her perfectly, she felt, as she wriggled her kimono-clad shoulders against it.

'Bob Boyne was absolutely bloody this morning,' he said, turning his head to look up at her from her lap. In the dimmed light she looked quite beautiful, though he knew she wasn't. Her long face, finely chiselled features and pale English rose complexion were indubitably attractive, pleasant, friendly, but not beautiful. He had often urged her to let her soft, flaxen hair grow long, but without success.

'Oh hell.' She had forgotten to ask about Boyne's visit. 'What happened?'

'It's getting nasty. Very. He insists I fire thirty more people.

To cut personnel overheads as he puts it. I said it couldn't be done, but he ignored me. He said we're living above our means, that I haven't acclimatised myself to thinking of Pendletons as a small agency in London. Prune it back thoroughly, he keeps repeating, and it will grow all the stronger.'

'But you can't. You just can't. The agency would disintegrate. Firing that many would get into *Campaign*. Our clients would hear. The best people would leave. It would be disastrous.'

'I said all that. But I might as well have been talking to myself. It makes me furious because we're making fair profits already. Twelve per cent on our income, which is almost as much as Isaacs and Isaacs make, according to their annual report. And they're not doing too badly! But Pendletons' target is twenty per cent. So we're eight per cent below par. Or only just above fifty per cent of target, as Boyne insists on putting it. Nobody makes twenty per cent mind you. Except for a couple of tiny subsidiaries in Atlanta and Singapore. Boyne just uses the twenty per cent figure to beat all us local managers with.'

'Is our twelve per cent better than average? Worldwide?'

'It's a bit less. Worldwide we make about sixteen and a half per cent. But there's lots of countries doing lots worse. In Germany we just about break even. In Italy and Spain we've been losing money for years. Twelve per cent isn't bad by comparison. Boyne insists that in a buoyant advertising market like the UK it's easy to make more. Then he repeats the company adage, "Profit is the first cost", climbs into a 747 and buggers off.'

'Profit is the first cost?'

'It means first you decide what profit you want to make. Then you tailor all your costs to make sure you make it. It's bullshit. Destructive bullshit.'

If only he were a foot taller, Flora thought looking down at him, he would be dazzling. He was still fit and supple, lean and muscular; he still rowed, played cricket and swam; he wore no glasses, had no crowns, his skin was clear and his opal eyes sparkled; only his white hair betrayed his age, together with increasingly frequent spinal pains. She did not love him, but she admired and adored him. And here he was, the powerful Chairman and Chief Executive of one of the country's top advertising agencies, who had only to whisper his wishes within its portals for them to be instantly obeyed, his head in her lap, fragile, uncertain and destructible. She wanted to ask him if he thought his job was in jeopardy, but couldn't find the right words so said nothing.

'He's coming back next week. And he wants me to have a list of people to be fired. Naming the names.'

'What are you going to do?'

'I don't know.' He knew that he should not be talking so freely with Flora, but he trusted her. And she cared and understood. Whereas Ellen, his wife, obsessed with running her Oxfam shop, did neither. Not that he viewed this as a reason for criticism; he was delighted that she was so absorbed in, and so enjoyed, her work. He looked at his watch. He must go.

'Did you tell him about Larsons?'

'No. It would only have made things worse.'

'You're mad. Crazy. He's bound to find out.'

'I had lunch with Des Digby yesterday. I think we'll keep the business. I think I know what to do.' Not having seen Flora the previous night he had had time to consider how best to tell her about his lunch without going into too much detail and without communicating Des's criticisms, which would discourage and demotivate her.

Flora was anxious to know what Des Digby had said, but for the moment her thoughts were still on Bob Boyne. 'If he finds out about Larsons from somewhere else, from *Campaign* or somewhere, you're scuppered. You know that. You should've told him. You could phone him now, if he's back in New York.'

'He's in Hong Kong, sorting out old David Newsome. Don't fret. It'll be all right.'

You optimistic idiot, Flora thought as she leaned forward to kiss him, and his hand slid inside her kimono, and they started to make love again.

' . . . of the Pan Am passengers are still in hospital, thirteen of them in a critical condition. . . .'

'Switch off. Let's go to bed.'

'Not just yet. I gotta read this damn Splashasoap marketing crap again. You go.'

Irving Gilbernetti was lying full stretch on the late-Victorian couch which he had re-covered with William Morris fabric. Rebecca Gilbernetti got up from her large white wicker chair, from which much of the paint had been scuffed, and switched off the set.

'I wonder,' mused Irving, 'whether any of them guys on the 747 is from Brooklyn?'

'Think you might know any of them?'

'No way. Even if I knew them at school I'd have forgotten 'em now. Except for Bernie Shulz. Remember we visited his store when we was over in '73? But there's no way he was in Karachi. To him Manhattan's a foreign country.'

Irving, wearing his Liberty print dressing-gown over his boxer shorts and T-shirt, his socked feet resting on the couch arm, looking like a slightly plumper version of Woody Allen without spectacles, grinned at his own joke and forced himself to concentrate on the Splashasoap marketing document. Rebecca glanced desultorily through *The Guardian*.

Summary of Advertising Research
1 Following the launch campaign unprompted awareness of the Splashasoap name was 11% and prompted awareness reached a 43% level.
2 Awareness of the advertising also had a low tendency, with only 6% (unprompted) and 21% (prompted) able to correctly identify the 'gunge and grime' sales proposition. The percentages were highest among the 45–64 age group (9% and 27%), and among the C1C2 social classes (8% and 25%).
3 Attitudes to the advertising among those who remembered (prompted) it were mixed, with 52% describing it as 'boring' on the adjectival checklist, 43% as 'unoriginal', 39% as 'old fashioned', while 44% said it was 'interesting' and 31% 'credible'....

Irving tried diligently to assimilate the figures, but they soon began to blur. He had drunk a little too much with Trevor at lunch-time, and it didn't agree with him. A jab of indigestion burned in his chest and he searched his pocket for his Setlers, seeking express relief.

'You shouldn't let them walk all over you,' Rebecca put down her paper. 'You shouldn't have to read all those reports. You're creative. Not a bloody market researcher.'

Rebecca had just left Camberwell Art School when Irving first met her, shortly after his arrival in London nineteen years before. She had never had a full-time job, but had kept afloat designing record sleeves and book jackets. She still treasured the sleeves she had done for the Moody Blues and The Kinks; she had been commissioned for a Rolling Stones album, but her hallucinogenic design had been rejected. She often wished she'd got it back and kept it, as her memory of it was now a little hazy. Her large, flat, pale face, upon which all the features seemed inappropriately small, nodded silent agreement with the Jill Tweedie article she was reading, as she unconsciously flicked her long, soft, slightly greying and slightly greasy ochre hair behind her.

'Far as I can see Hal and James do bugger all except get pissed with clients, and you do all the work. You're too soft, Irving, too bloody soft.'

'Honey, you don't know from nothing. So leave it alone. Please. I like gettin' in to the facts and figures. Always have. You know that.' He sounded neither convinced nor convincing as he lifted the report from his chest, on which it had been lying, and forced himself to focus once again on the poorly photocopied type:

Attitudinal Findings
1   Small-scale pilot research comprising 4 group discussions among C1C2 housewives aged 30–45 in London and South East, some of them regular users of Spashasoap or other liquid soaps, others aware of this product category but non-users themselves, threw up the following:
    (a) Most women believe ordinary soap and water to be drying to the skin, especially in so far as the face is concerned, but also when bathing, washing-up etc.
    (b) Liquid soaps are accepted to be less drying and to contain moisturising factors which therefore do not dry skin (or at least dry it on the lesser side conceptually).

(c) There is a positive dichotomy between users of liquid soaps and non-users on this dimension, with users believing the non-drying factor to be a purchase motivator while non users...

'What's going on with Joan?' Rebecca interrupted Irving's fragile concentration.

'Joan?... oh, Joan. The mastectomy went fine, Hal says. She'll probably be out next week. He says she's in depression; so who wouldn't be? You should go visit. Any time's OK in the private wing. Great we're on BUPA, eh?' Hal seized every opportunity to extol the benefits of belonging to BUPA, about which his wife was far from enthusiastic. Two days previously James Orr had tried to make them quit BUPA, because the agency could no longer afford it, but Hal and Irving had refused.

'I can't stand her, you know I can't. If she'd had kids instead of spending her time at horse shows it probably wouldn't have happened. All she cares about is bloody horses.'

'So it won't kill you to go talk about horses for half an hour.'

'Maybe.'

The deteriorating relationship between Irving, Hal and James was echoed in the relationships between their wives, each of whom blamed the other two partners for Gilbernetti, Orr and Burton's lack of success, and blamed their spouses – with varying degrees of intolerance and sympathy – for having got themselves involved with such inadequate partners in the first place. Irving, Hal and James were all well aware of this situation, though it was never mentioned, and they in turn responded to their wives' intolerance and sympathy with varying degrees of intolerance and sympathy. All six of them avoided connubial social gatherings whenever possible.

Rebecca had never found Irving's partners' wives congenial. They were both, in her eyes, archetypal middle-class, status-conscious businessmen's spouses, ambitious for their husbands and desperate to be rich, richer, richest, so they could live in big, bigger, biggest houses, drive in biggest cars, spend more on clothes and cosmetics and holidays. Whereas Rebecca's own attitudes to money were equivocal, as was evidenced by the style and décor of their small Highbury home, which was always scruffy, with kids' toys and clothes on the sanded wooden floor, on the stairs, in the kitchen and on all the chairs. Though she regularly grumbled that unlike most other middle-class mothers she had no cleaner or daily help, and was always short of money and nearly always overdrawn, she nonetheless had no desire to be very rich and suspected that she would be unable to cope with wealth ('not that there's the least likelihood of it happening, I should be so lucky').

Irving, though now utterly apolitical, had been an American communist in his teens; and she was still a member of the local Labour Party, though she hardly ever attended meetings ('with the kids to look after, what time do I have?').

Crowded on the walls of their sitting-room were some fine post-1917 Russian posters; two Vicki cartoons which they'd bought at a charity auction; three of Irving's own oils; a couple of her record sleeves carefully mounted; one of each of the children's early paintings ('we mustn't show favouritism'); a Beggerstaff Brothers' woodcut; an early Peter Blake, which they hoped was worth quite a lot; three West African wooden masks; a Steinberg foreshortened New York and the pièce de résistance above the mantelpiece, a large Edvard Munch lithograph.

The heavy metal sound of Iron Maiden percolating through the thin ceiling heralded the fact that Matt, their thirteen-year-old, had finished his homework and was preparing for bed. Only to an ear-shattering musical accompaniment, he claimed, could he fall asleep.

> . . . purchasers who were not heavy users (less than once on average per annum).
> (e) The deterrent factor to purchasing, among those non-users who accepted the product benefits, was its expense. Splashasoap is perceived by this sizeable sector as being in the luxury, indulgent mode. . . .

Standing up, straightening her russet kaftan over her paunchy tummy, and bending to pull the fraying corner of the worn

Anatolian kelim rug straight, Rebecca moved over to her husband. She watched him struggling with the market research statistics she knew he could not grasp, and in a gesture of affection that was now far from common she ruffled his wispy hair. 'Leave all that crap,' she said quietly, 'let's go to bed. . . . '

Had Irving Gilbernetti enjoyed, or more likely suffered, the benefit of a classical education he might at that moment have cried 'Eureka!' As it was, he threw the market research report in the air, hitting his wife a glancing blow on the cheek, jumped to his feet, shouted 'Expensive. That's it. Expensive.' He hugged his wife hard enough to squeeze her thin again, kissed her recently assaulted cheek, and with his arm around her pushed her clumsily towards the bedroom, neglecting to turn off either the light or the costly electric fan heater behind them.

' . . . thirteen of them in a critical condition. . . . '

'He's gay. Did you know?' Harry Adams, putting on his red-framed spectacles, indicated that he meant the newscaster, who was by now indulging in silent chit-chat with his lady colleague as the screen darkened and faded them out.

Lying full length on his spotless yellow settee, in his matching fawn silk dressing-gown, Harry looked down at the small figure with green spiky hair snuggled against him. Harry had loaned him one of his Ted Lapidus cotton shirts. It was far too big, which made the small boy look even more succulently pretty.

'I'd heard he was,' Paul O'Reilly replied, 'but I wasn't sure if it was true.'

'As a nine bob note,' Harry replied. 'I had him a couple of years back. Lovely guy. Lives with an Italian architect. They had a tenth anniversary party a few months ago at their place on the Isle of Dogs. You'd be amazed who was there.'

' . . . Pa . . . a . . . an Am', the choir jingled, as Paul stretched awkwardly across the white carpeted floor to switch off the set. He scrabbled back on to the settee, squeezing himself between Harry and the cushions, and looked around again at Harry's high-ceilinged mid-Victorian drawing-room just off Queen's Gate. Everything in the room was pale and muted, and looked as though it had just been dusted: from the small white piano by the windows to the Ming china on the large mantelpiece, from the three pretty pastel Adrian Georges to the grey china cat in the fireplace, from the heavy beige curtains to the innumerable scatter cushions in shades of yellow and fading greens. The only jarring note was Paul's denims and bright blue braces, black T-shirt and Doctor Martin boots in the corner by the alabaster lamp, where they had been thrown as he and Harry had jointly pulled them off two hours earlier. Harry had since carefully hung away his own clothes in his bedroom wardrobe.

They had met that evening for the first time, in The Queensbury, a pub neither of them frequented often, because it was too often frequented by other gays. Each had promised himself that he would just pop in for a quick drink on the way home. They had started chatting, quickly discovered they were both in advertising, had another drink and then another . . . there was no doubt, Harry thought, that Paul was the prettiest boy in the pub. His fine bone structure and small, sharp features, his tiny mouth and perfect lips were entrancing. While Paul, in turn, was flattered to be courted by one of the biggies of the advertising business: Harry Adams, partner in the legendary Adams Coventry McAndrew, whom he had never dreamed might be gay, who exuded wealth and charm, and who obviously fancied him. Harry was, Paul guessed, well into his forties, but his body was still lissome, he was tanned and fit, and although his nose was a bit big and his eyes too close together, he was unusually attractive. He was, thought Paul, easily the most striking man in The Queensbury that evening. He had presence.

'D'you think you'll hold on to Larsons?' Harry asked, moving his hand down to hold Paul's, which had been resting on the side of his colourful head.

'Oh yeah. Me and Tom have done a fantastic campaign. Tom Nathan's my copywriter. He's great, Tom. They're researching it, though, which is a bloody pain.'

'What is it? Your campaign?' Harry squeezed Paul's hand affectionately.

Paul was silent for a moment. He knew he ought not to answer, though he believed advertising people made too much fuss about secrets: they're just like schoolkids, it's all a game. What difference could it make if Harry knew about the campaign? Harry couldn't steal it, or even harm it. It was a great commercial, and that was what counted. What could it matter if Harry knew?

'Are you pitching for the business?' he asked.

It was Harry's turn to stay silent. Should he lie? Should he be truthful, but add a 'we're not really interested in it' rider? Should he just change the subject, and leave it at that?

'I'm not involved myself. Not at all. But I think someone called Rigby or Philby or something spoke to Mike Coventry on the phone the other day.' His right leg, underneath Paul, was beginning to feel cramped. He moved it free, wrapping it gently but tightly around the boy's body.

'That'll be Des Digby. He's Marketing Manager. A right sod, he is.'

Harry doubted whether his new-found catamite quite knew what he was saying. 'Does your friend Tom know you're gay?'

'I don't know. I pretend I've got girls, but he don't seem interested anyway.'

'Is he?'

'Gay? Tom Nathan? He fucks any piece of skirt he can get his hands up.' He paused briefly. 'Didya know Fred's trying to persuade me and Tom to come to your place?'

'Fred?'

'The headhunter. She says you're on for a big bit of business. But she won't tell what it is though. Is it Larsons?'

'We . . . we're pitching all the time. Just now we're the hottest shop in town.'

Harry hoped most fervently that Bill McAndrew was not blurting their prospective client pitch list to all and sundry.

'People say ACM's a bit of a sweat shop,' Paul said, being deliberately cheeky.

'Who says?'

'Just people. Most people.'

'Rubbish.' Harry deplored the way ridiculous rumours swirl endlessly through the advertising business. 'What's Tom Nathan like?'

'Great. Great to work with. He scares the shit out of the suits.'

'The suits?'

'The account executives, you wally. And the directors and that lot. All the ones that come to work in suits.'

The slang was new to Harry, but hardly difficult to understand. He pondered how to get the conversation back to Larsons and Splashasoap. Fate had been extraordinarily kind in delivering pretty Paul O'Reilly into his embrace. Even when he had discovered Paul worked at Pendletons, and had invited him home, it had not occurred to him that the boy might be working on Splashasoap. His desire for Paul had been sheer, unadulterated lust. It was rare and extraordinary good fortune that his lust might provide him with an additional bonus.

'If your campaign's so good,' he asked innocently, 'why do they need to research it . . . ?' But even as he finished the question he felt small Paul's fingers beginning to stroke him again, and he felt the boy's head wriggle down. . . .

' . . . for moments of joy . . . of bliss . . . of mystery . . .'

As Tom Nathan switched off his least favourite commercial his telephone rang. It was the second night running he'd seen that crappy Pierre Robert commercial, and it appalled him more with each viewing. How could Pendletons hope to be a great agency if it allowed itself to produce such unadulterated rubbish?

'Allo.'

'Tom?'

'It was Jenny Sandford. He recognised her squeaky voice immediately. ' 'Ow are you, Jenny?'

'I'm OK. It had taken her all evening and two large glasses of Liebfraumilch to build up enough courage to make the call.

'I was just going to kip,' Tom said.

'Yes . . . so am I. Am I going to see you again ever?'

'Course. We'll bump into each other at work, I expect.'

'I meant . . . after last Thursday. . . . '

Last Thursday, after Alan Gilmore's leaving party in The Monkey Puzzle, they had ended up spending the night together. It had been good fun, but he wasn't proposing to make a great romance of it. Anyway, she'd told him she was screwing Simon Booth and he didn't intend sharing a fuck with that prat.

'How's Simon?'

'I don't think I'm going to see him any more.'

'You can't miss 'im around the office. Well I can't, more's the pity.'

Jenny was far too nervous to respond to such banter. 'I . . . I'd like to see you again.'

'Well, I don't know,' Tom replied. 'Shall I . . . d'you want me to jump in a cab and come over?'

He could almost hear the tension drain from her body. 'That would be really, really nice.'

'Pierre Renoir . . . for moments of joy . . . of bliss . . . of mystery . . .'

The shitty Pierre Renoir commercial reminded Ralph Isaacs of something, and he got up from the black leather and stainless steel Bauhaus sofa on which he had been sitting. His wife was already in bed, upstairs in their Mayfair house, and he was about to follow her but stopped to make a call. 'Chas? Sorry to phone so late. You in bed?'

The editor of *Campaign* informed Ralph that not only was he in bed, but that he had been asleep when the phone rang.

'OK. OK. Sorry. Only I'm not around much tomorrow so I thought you'd want to know now.' Ralph Isaacs, as the editor of *Campaign* well knew, made phone calls whenever the thought struck him: early morning and late at night, Saturday, Sunday, Christmas Day, whenever – if Ralph had something to say, he liked to say it immediately.

'Larsons have asked Pendletons to repitch. . . It's worth five or six million. . . . No, we're not on the list . . . maybe because we've got competitive business in other countries. I dunno . . . Adams Coventry's on the list, so's that shitty GOB shop; yeah, I think that's all. . . . How the fuck should I know? You want stories or don't you? . . . Yeah. Good night.' Ralph slammed the receiver into its cradle and turned off the light. $600 million for a shitty agency like Pendletons! Well that little chat would bring the price down a bit.

V
Revelations

As he surveyed the line of silent, naked, middle-aged businessmen Chris Beaumont wondered whether all of them had as many worries, wondered whether they too were wrestling with intractable business problems to which rational, justifiable solutions did not exist. They were all over forty and, presumably, in top jobs; though deprived of their status-proclaiming apparel it was impossible to be sure. Without being able to pinpoint why, he was sure that a line of nude manual labourers would look quite different. Maybe it was their haircuts or their hands, their faces or their gestures, their pale paunches or their varicose veins or some combination of all of those and more, which together semaphored their owners' executive status to anyone who knew the code.

A memory of his first interview at Keeble flashed across his mind, when his old economics tutor had said, 'It's astonishing how things have changed, Beaumont, since the war. Before 1939 you could tell as soon as a lad walked in the room what social class he came from, what kind of school he'd attended. Didn't matter a jot how much his mother had toffed him up. The public school lads looked healthy, with clear skin and tidy hair cuts. The working-class boys had acne and looked sickly. It was their wretched diets. And the ones that got here had to work so hard they never saw fresh air.

'It's all different now. Since the war you all get fed properly. You all get out on the games field. And I can't tell the difference any more. Damn good thing too.'

As his companions silently put on their underwear and socks, Chris recognised many of them by sight: their faces, buttocks, bellies, even their private parts. By now many of them were nearly dressed, in their dark executive suits, white shirts, dark ties and brogue shoes, and were neatly tying their ties and combing their mostly balding pates in the long mirrors, still in eerie silence. Chris had been swimming at the RAC clubhouse in Pall Mall two or three mornings a week for nearly two years and had never yet spoken to anyone. Only very rarely had he seen anyone speak to anyone. Each morning about four dozen men arrived with their briefcases from seven o'clock onwards, undressed communally, swam in the cavernous Egyptianesque pool, climbed out after their regulation fifteen or twenty or thirty lengths, showered, dressed again and left with their briefcases but without having uttered a word. It was like a religious ritual, a sacred ceremony in which all those involved had taken a vow of Trappist silence; but it was only businessmen, having a swim, keeping in trim.

The October morning was bright but chill, and, having come straight from the warm pool with his hair still damp Chris shivered as he left the club's grand portals and walked to his waiting driver, past a queue of five or six other chauffeur-driven limousines similarly attendant upon their masters' crawl and breast-strokes. Chris's driver had collected him from his home in Kensington at seven-fifteen, and it was now almost eight o'clock. He had arranged to meet the Managing Director of Pierre Renoir for breakfast at the Connaught at eight, in order to resolve the still vexed question of the Chenonceaux commercial's sound level.

He had with him a memo from the sound recording studio, full of detailed and incomprehensible technical data proving conclusively (he had been assured) that the decibel count was as high as it could go; and he was reading the memo for the third time while pouring himself a second cup of the Connaught's coffee – the waiter as always being absent, when needed – when the concierge arrived with the message that his client had had to go to another business breakfast and so would be unable to turn up, sorry.

That, thought Chris as he decided to miss out on breakfast, paid for his coffee and left, is the writing big and unmistakable on the wall. When a client, particularly a client like Pierre Renoir Perfumes, fails to turn up for an appointment and sends only the most cursory of apologies, the game is over. Knowing the way Gertie Tannenbaum ruled her empire, it meant that all her minions had either been told or had sensed that the axe was about to fall. Misfortunes come not single spies but in battalions, he mumbled to himself remembering his O-level *Hamlet*.

In the half-hour between his swim and leaving the Connaught the sky had turned television-screen grey, and the wind grown colder. The autumn morning, Chris felt, had suddenly turned to winter. Having brought no overcoat he found himself shivering again as the Connaught's top-hatted doorman opened his car door for him, and he switched the heater on to full as his car sped into Grosvenor Square.

The impending loss of Pierre Renoir could not have come at a more unfortunate, or unfair, moment. It had nothing whatsoever to do with Pendletons' performance in London, despite the decibel level brouhaha: that was a symptom, not a cause. Pendletons was about to be fired, globally for certain, because Gertie Tannenbaum, in her ninety-seventh-floor Manhattan eyrie, had whimsically so decreed. But in London it would mean the loss of nearly another £2 million turnover, nearly another £300,000 in agency income. The immediate, short-term effect on the agency's profits would be disastrous. Because most of the advertising was created in New York Pierre Renoir – like many multinational accounts – was exceedingly profitable elsewhere. Adding British sound-tracks to US film footage was not, no matter how much aggravation it involved, a particularly time-consuming activity. Handling Pierre Renoir in London had been, as Pendletons' time-sheet and cost-analyses had consistently shown, money for jam. (The shrewd Ms Tannenbaum seemed not to have yet cottoned on to this; or maybe she had, and knew she extorted so much blood, sweat and tears from Pendletons in New York that she didn't mind the agency making a few bucks out of her in faraway places.)

With Boyne already screaming for more savings, with Larsons still at risk – though he was now optimistic about keeping it – and with the loss of Pierre Renoir certain, the outlook was far from cheerful; but as always Chris dutifully put on a cheerful smile as he entered the agency and greeted the early arrivals. And forcing himself to look cheerful made him feel cheerful.

Having phoned Flora on the internal, a foolish and incautious act in which he rarely indulged, in order to confirm, unnecessarily, that they would be meeting that evening as planned, he was still feeling unjustifiably cheerful when his telephone rang at nine thirty-five. His cheerfulness evaporated instantly his secretary announced that it was Gail Hawkins on the line.

It was Wednesday and Gail Hawkins – the brightest, prettiest and most aggressive of *Campaign* magazine's coven of bright, pretty and aggressive journalists – would not be telephoning to discuss the weather or inquire about his health. For *Campaign* Wednesday was press day. So an early Wednesday telephone call meant their newshounds had a story about you, about which they have been biding their time, waiting to see if it appears anywhere else, waiting to see if they have an exclusive for publication on Thursday.

'Hi, Gail. How can I help you?'

'I'm sorry to have to call you about this, Chris. But I've heard bad news.'

All *Campaign* reporters had their own flock of agencies which it was their responsibility to track, to know intimately, so they could quickly hack out a story without too many inaccuracies and without needing to waste much time investigating the background. Pendletons was one of Gail's agencies, and she knew it was having a rough time.

'Really? What bad news?' Chris would say nothing until she revealed her story. She might be referring to Pierre Renoir; or to Larsons; or worst of all to something he didn't yet know about. *Campaign* journalists, ears permanently skimming the ground, often heard rumours of client moves well ahead of the agencies about to be sacked.

'I hear Larsons is moving.'

'Moving?' Surely they could not have decided to move without seeing the agencies' presentations? Peter Dalrymple would never behave like that.

'You must know. Don't you?'

'That they're moving? No.'

'Well it's up for pitches.' Gail liked Chris. He was more honest with her than most of the agency bosses she dealt with.

He only lied when he was cornered and had no alternative, whereas most agency people seemed to lie to her for the hell of it.

'Yes. It's up for pitches, and we're repitching. Larsons felt they ought to look around after having been with us for so long. It's just a periodic review. Doesn't mean anything at all. We're bound to keep it.'

'That's not what people are saying, Chris. You know Adams Coventry are in the race?'

'Of course I do. Larsons have kept me fully informed,' Chris lied. He had not known about ACM. And it was bad news.

'Do you know who else is on their list?' Gail asked. Her editor had told her about ACM and GOB, but there might be others; and GOB seemed so odd a choice that she wanted to have it confirmed.

'I'm sure you know already, Gail. You don't need my help.' He was striving to sound confident and friendly, but it was becoming increasingly difficult.

'Do you want to give me a quote for publication?' she asked.

'No thanks.'

'Sorry about the news.'

'Don't worry. I'm not.'

As he put the phone down he summoned his secretary, and began to dictate a telex he had already drafted in his mind several days before.

> To: Bob Boyne
> Today heard Larsons is undertaking agency review. This is one of their regular periodic reviews and we have no reason to be too worried. We are already well ahead with preparation of a new campaign which we will be presenting to them next week. Am reasonably confident. Will keep you informed.
> With best regards,
>
> Chris

The stupid bastard, Bob Boyne thought, when he read it in his hotel room in Athens. Who does he think he's fooling? He must have known about this for weeks. Maybe months. And if he didn't he's even more fucking incompetent than I thought. He'll have to go.

Peter Dalrymple's comparative lack of success puzzled Peter Dalrymple as much as it puzzled others. He was conscious, painfully conscious, that all through his childhood he had been the cleverest boy in class; that at Cambridge he had gained his first without undue labour; that after graduating a cornucopia of choices had been open to him: he could have become a don; or a barrister, or entered the Foreign Office; but instead he opted for industry, and until his mid-thirties he had been an executive starlet. *Management Today*, shortly after its launch, had profiled him, with two others, as Britain's Three Young Businessmen to watch. Then it had all fizzled out.

Naturally it had not been apparent at first. He had got stuck at Marketing Director level at Reckitts because they had too many good people chasing too few jobs (the company simply wasn't expanding fast enough) and his immediate superior was only a few years older than himself. He had moved sideways to be Marketing Director of Larsons, with the prospect of becoming Managing Director and then Chairman quite quickly. It hadn't happened.

He was not bitter, but he felt aggrieved. And puzzled. He would like to have been able to blame his luck, but he was far too wise to do so. He had had bad luck, certainly, but like Napoleon he believed generals make their own luck. Nor could it be his intelligence. He was no longer, he feared, as brilliantly clever as he had been when young, but he was still the brightest bloke in the company. He devoured complex documents and analysed their contents with incomparable rapidity and skill.

No, it had to be a failing of character, of personality. But what was it? He had tentatively asked others, which wasn't easy, but had obtained no satisfactory answers. Sometimes he suspected he was insufficiently competitive, insufficiently committed to success – but he worked as hard as anyone in the company; sometimes he suspected he was insufficiently impatient, insufficiently bad tempered – but he was renowned for his inability to suffer fools gladly; sometimes he suspected he was insufficiently ruthless, insufficiently tough on his subordinates – but he never shirked from issuing reprimands when they were necessary, and took unpleasant decisions when they had to be taken.

Admittedly he had noticed of late a tendency to daydream, to lose his concentration more easily than of yore. But that, he believed, was a chicken-and-egg problem; he was underextended at Larsons, he had been doing the job too long and it no longer stretched him. He was bored. No wonder he daydreamed.

And he was daydreaming that Wednesday morning, of punting to Grantchester on a sultry summer afternoon, of the Cam's cool water trickling down his arm from the pole, of the river unaccountably hushed and deserted, when his secretary brought in his plastic cup of coffee from the machine, and his post.

'There's one marked "strictly personal" so I didn't open it, Mr Dalrymple. I hope that's all right.' She was alluding to the fatuous, old-fashioned and widely disregarded Larsons' rule that all letters should be addressed to the company rather than to individuals and that personal correspondence was not permitted.

'Of course, thanks pet.' Strictly personal? Unusual. London postmark, unrecognisable typewriter. Tearing the envelope open he pulled out a sheet of plain bond paper on which was typed, a trifle inexpertly:

> We regret having to bring this to your attention, Mr Dalrymple, but you should know your marketing manager, Mr Desmond Digby, has lately, at the Vanderbilt nightclub – which is little more than a licensed brothel – been enjoying the company of so-called hostesses (equals, if you will excuse the word Mr Dalrymple, whores) at the expense, and no doubt on the expense account of one Mr Hal Burton, a partner in the advertising agency Gilbernetti Orr and Burton.
>
> We repeat that we regret bringing to your attention this distasteful matter, but as we understand Messrs Gilbernetti, Orr and Burton are currently in contest for your advertising account, it is therefore only proper

that you should be acquainted with their seedy business methods.

We also regret that this letter must remain anonymous, but you may rest assured that it is God's truth in every respect.

Peter Dalrymple read the letter rapidly, unable to absorb its contents. Then he read it again very slowly, dwelling on each word and phrase, subconsciously praying they did not say what they palpably did say, that he had somehow misread them.

Never before in his thirty years in business had he received such a letter. He had heard of such things happening, of course: but like motor accidents and being struck by lightning, they were things that happened only to others. His immediate reaction was to summon Digby and face him with the accusation. But on second thoughts he decided it would be wiser to give himself time to calm down. He was trembling with confused anger and anxiety, and it would be sensible to analyse the situation and the options open to him carefully, and unemotionally. Unconsciously his hand went to his jacket pocket and clenched his pocket Bible, which brought some solace.

At that moment his telephone rang, and his secretary informed him that Gail Hawkins of *Campaign* wanted to speak to him.

'*Campaign*? Ask her what she wants.'

He held the receiver to his ear and re-read the anonymous letter yet again. The best thing would be to tear it into tiny pieces and throw it in the bin – anonymous defamatory letters are despicable, invariably untruthful, and should be ignored. The use of the Deity's name in the last sentence was especially upsetting. Yet ... Desmond Digby was an idiot. He had not been Peter's first choice for the job. Peter had judged from the start that Digby wasn't right, either intellectually or morally. But Peter's first two choices had turned the job down and, by then almost in desperation, he had accepted that Digby was probably the best he could get; Larsons was not one of those fashionable companies at which the brightest and the best young marketing men want to work.

'She says it's urgent and important, and she's got to speak to you personally.'

'Oh . . . all right, put her through. . . .Hallo, Gail, how's the gutter press these days?'

Gail Hawkins ignored the jibe. If you worked on an advertising trade magazine like *Campaign* it was essential to develop a thick hide. Anyway, she had met Peter Dalrymple at several marketing and advertising functions, and viewed him as a humourless wimp, not worth bandying insults with. 'We hear you've fired Pendletons and moved your account to Gilbernetti, Orr and Burton,' she said, being deliberately provocative.

'Gilbernetti, Orr and . . . who?' It was that bloody agency of Des Digby's friends. Surely Des could not already have promised them the business? 'I don't know what you're talking about.' Peter Dalrymple disliked lying and was far from good at it.

'Oh come on, Peter, I haven't got all day. We'll be running the story on the front page whatever you say. So you can either give me the facts or I'll have to cobble them together as best I can.'

He knew she was not bluffing. *Campaign* was notorious, most advertising people believed, for publishing rumours and half-truths. 'We have invited certain agencies to present for our Splashasoap account. I'm not naming them. And Pendletons will be re-presenting and may well keep the business. That's all I'm going to say.'

'Is Gilbernetti, Orr and Burton one of the agencies?'

'Gilbernetti, Orr and Burton? I've never even met them.'

'But they are on the shortlist?'

'I told you. I've not met them. Ever. And I'm not saying any more.'

'But why are you considering moving your account? Are your sales falling? Are you dissatisfied with Pendletons?'

'Our sales are fine. Buoyant in fact. And we've been very happy in our long association with Pendletons. But every so often we think it right to review the situation. That's all this is. A review . . . and now I really must go to a meeting. . . .'

Were Peter Dalrymple not a religious man his mental

language, as he put down the phone, would have been a great deal cruder. For first thing tomorrow, when the story was revealed, he would be inundated with telephone calls and telexes, with letters and parcels, with gimmicks and gimcrack ideas from almost every one of the country's four hundred advertising agencies, all of them pestering him to visit them, all of them convinced that they and they alone were the ideal agency for Larsons, most of them claiming to have met him on some occasion or other, and all of them determined to win his business.

The disruption and confusion would be chaotic; and he had more important problems to resolve, he remembered, as he folded the letter and stuffed it into his jacket pocket, with his Bible.

As Simon Booth entered their office, Tom Nathan was reading aloud to Paul O'Reilly, with heavy sarcasm, the final paragraph of Chris Beaumont's 'All Staff' memo on pink paper:

> '... Finally I wish to emphasise that Mr Peter Dalrymple, the Marketing Director of Larsons, has personally assured me this is a routine review, and is no reflection of any kind on the excellent service they have received from Pendletons over the years.
> 'The creative department have already produced an outstanding new campaign for Splashasoap, which we are currently researching, and I have every confidence that this is a pitch Pendletons are going to win!
> 'Good luck to everyone involved.

'... and there will be no whitewash in the White House, eh Simon? What shit! Who does he think will believe it?' Tom Nathan asked rhetorically as he tore the memo into little pieces and threw them like confetti over Simon's head.

'I don't know why you're being so bloody sarcastic. Most of it's true. And he seems to like your campaign. So let's see if the public agrees with him.'

'Do you have any ties which don't 'ave measles, Simon?' Tom asked.

'Yes ... no. ... Is the finished storyboard ready? I've got a taxi waiting downstairs. I'm supposed to be over at Greg Hamilton's with it in five minutes. And he's in Chelsea.'

'Then you're gonna be late, my boy. So sit down and take the dead weight of your little account executive legs.'

Simon glanced around the small office. As Tom and Paul were occupying the only two chairs, and were clearly not intending to relinquish them, and as the only desk was covered with bits of the Splashasoap storyboard, which had been drawn up immaculately and in detail in order to be researched, Tom's invitation to sit down was also rhetorical. Paul was carefully but unhurriedly sticking the storyboard drawings on to cards with spray glue, and Simon could see the job was unlikely to be finished for at least another ten minutes. He would be at least twenty minutes late for Greg Hamilton. Damn Tom and Paul!

The walls of Tom and Paul's office were cluttered with scraps ripped from magazines: with a collection of photographers' and art studios' visiting cards; with typesettings of headlines from ads now long gone to press; with pictures of models whom they might one day want to use; with proofs of ads they admired, mostly American; with a Polaroid of Tom at the Christmas party, dressed as a pirate and apparently trying to rape three of the agency's secretaries simultaneously; with a calendar produced by one of London's leading design companies, still at July; and with a fat plastic turd which Tom had greatly enjoyed putting on various executives' seats earlier in the year; all pinned up higgledy-piggledy and, once up, seemingly completely forgotten by the office's two inhabitants.

And on the floor in one corner, propped against the wall and looking rejected, was the Runalong advertisement. 'Have Runalong seen your ad yet?' Simon asked, knowing the answer.

'The bitch turned it down,' small Paul replied, as he checked that he had pasted the storyboard frames squarely on to their mounts. 'It was too creative for her, and that's the truth.'

'You mean the bleedin' Vicar sold it down the river. 'E couldn't tell a great ad from the 'ole in his arse, our lovely Vicar.'

'What did the client say, then?' Simon inquired, running his long fingers through his hair, and enjoying their failure to get the ad approved.

'Usual shit . . . I do *like* it. I do *like* it a lot.' Tom's mimickry, as Simon remembered from his arch enemy's cabaret turns at Oxford, was splendidly apt. 'It's frightfully . . . *creative*. . . . I congratulate you, I really do . . . but somehow it isn't quite *us*. . . . I mean it's all *our* fault really . . . we're a *frightfully* fuddy-duddy sort of company you see . . . and an unclad girl on her *own*, in a forest. . . . I mean it is rather *perverted* . . . not that you *meant* it that way. I'm sure . . . At which point,' Tom reverted from Wiltshire dowager to Stepney costermonger, 'the Vicar jumps in with his hobnailed boots, bow tie flailing, Meerschaum stinking, and says yes ma'am, no ma'am, three bags full ma'am, and can I lick your arse while I'm at it ma'am, leavin' me and Pauly up shit creek without a Pentel.'

Simon grinned, both at Tom's story and at his discomfiture, then asked, 'How much longer are you going to be, Paul? I'd better phone Greg Hamilton and say I'll be late.' But as he reached for the phone it rang, and he picked it up.

'Is Tom Nathan or Paul there?' a husky female voice asked.'

'Both of them. Who's calling?'

'Fred.'

'It's for you-hoo. It's Fred.' Simon handed Tom the receiver.

'No,' Tom rasped, 'no. I'll call you back. In ten.' Tom banged the receiver into its cradle as Paul finally completed the storyboard and handed it to Simon, who was now grinning broadly, again.

'So who's being headhunted then? You lucky beggars! For lots more lolly, I'll bet. Where are you going, then? BMP? Or CDP? Or is it ACM?'

'It's none of your bloody business,' Paul said, 'So keep your toffee nose out of our affairs.' For two days he had been yearning to tell Tom about his evening with Harry Adams, about everything Harry had told him, about the engulfing excitement of being with so famous an adman. It would have to be an edited, cleaned-up version of course; but so far he hadn't dared say anything.

'An' while we're on the subject of little secrets,' Tom said, as Simon turned to leave, 'I 'ear you've been screwin' that Jenny tart in accounts. 'Ow is she? Good fuck?'

As he rushed with the Splashasoap storyboard to the cantankerous lift, Simon heard Tom roar with laughter.

Mike Coventry was unusual among advertising men. Not only was he an exceptional account planner and market analyst, but he was also an energetic and enthusiastic new business chaser. Proficient as they might be at selling their clients' products, only a handful of admen were much good at cold canvassing, at personal salesmanship. Whenever the news that a client was loose broke in *Campaign* dozens of them quickly mailed a brochure, usually out of date, with a brief covering letter; dozens more tried, usually unsuccessfully, to telephone the client. All of them knew that by the time the story had been revealed in the press they were likely to be too late. The client would have drawn up his short list and might even have made his final choice. But they nonetheless felt impelled, like greyhounds after an electric hare, to give artificial chase. Few had ever worked as sales people, few had even so much as sold jumble at a charity stall; and few had the innate, exuberant confidence of the born salesman.

Ralph Isaacs, as we have seen, despite his stupendous success had never personally solicited business, though his cousin Stanley forced himself to do so; Chris Beaumont was far too aware of Pendletons' inadequacies to sell his agency with unimpaired gusto; James Orr, who thought of himself as a businessman and financial manager, reckoned it was Hal Burton's job to peddle the agency, but Hal Burton was not much good at it; most clients found Harry Adam's disdainful manner off-putting (apparent disdain for clients being a besetting sin of advertising agency folk); Bill McAndrew and Irving Gilbernetti, as Creative Directors, were not expected to chase business; and nor was Mike Coventry – since account planners are, by repute, backroom boys rather than barrow boys.

But Mike Coventry, despite his stammer, loved it.

Much to his colleagues' surprise, his ballooning activities had been billowing nicely. Aaron Thistlethwaite, the multimillionaire founder, president, keen balloonist and occasionally benevolent despot of Thistlethwaites Olde English Jammes – the last word being one of Aaron's proudest inventions – had promised to visit the agency 'to see what you young lads can do for me them McCanns monkeys can't'.

'He doesn't believe in market research,' Harry Adams was saying, as the young(ish) lads discussed how to handle the prospective client's impending visit, 'at least not unless it flatters him, and confirms his prejudices.'

'I haven't g . . . got that impression,' Mike Coventry disagreed, the head on the end of his long neck resting on his hands, his elbows on the knees of the khaki drills he almost always wore.

'Haven't you heard about the time Mark Ramage of Dorlands made a presentation to him? Just before McCanns got the business, that was.' Harry Adams rubbed the lenses of his pink-framed glasses with relish, as he began the story. 'Dorlands had done some research and discovered that awareness of Thistlethwaites Jammes was low, far below Hartleys, Chivers, Robertsons or even Tiptree. Which proved, in their view, that Thistlethwaites needed much more advertising. And much better advertising, which – surprise, surprise – Dorlands offered to provide.'

'So Ramage opens the presentation to Aaron Thistlethwaite with a chart showing Thistlethwaites' low awareness score, but gets no further. Aaron screams "it's lies, lies", then switches on his intercom and barks to his Sales Director, "Mr Smith, tell me, who is the most famous jam maker in Britain?" "You are, of course, Mr Thistlethwaite," answers the obsequious lackey, anxious to protect his mortgage repayments and his children's private education.

'Thistlethwaite then turns to Ramage and shouts "My PR people say my name is in the papers more than nine hundred times a year. The public recognises me wherever I go. This morning when my Bentley stopped at the lights a taxi driver said 'Good morning, Mr Thistlethwaite!' And you have the bloody nerve to come in here, into my own office with market research which kids of two could tell you was bollocks. I'm famous Mr Ramage, *famous*! There's lies, damn lies and statistics, Mr Ramage. Maybe you didn't know that. But it's true. Unlike your bloody market research. Now get out of my office! NOW!" '

By the end of Harry's story Mike Coventry and Bill McAndrew were giggling like the aforementioned kids of two. Harry was a wonderful raconteur. And while they were in such a good humour he decided quickly to change the subject.

'I've been meaning to tell you,' Harry went on, loosening his Paul Smith paisley tie, 'something else entirely. I was having a drink with a chum last night and there were some loud-mouthed creatives from Pendletons in the bar. I can't believe how stupid some agency people are.'

Mike and Bill both knew of their partner's sexual proclivities, and Mike wondered idly which gay bar he would have been drinking in.

'So?' Bill asked.

'Well, these two Pendletons creatives were pissed. And they were describing their Splashasoap campaign. The campaign they're going to present to Larsons. They described it in full technicolour detail. I couldn't believe my ears.'

By now all trace of giggling had vanished, and Mike and Bill listened intently as Harry revealed Tom Nathan and Paul O'Reilly's campaign.

'What crap,' Bill McAndrew said as Harry finished, 'there's no idea there. No idea at all.'

'B . . . but it's an interesting strategy, just . . . justifying the premium price on a moisturising platform. F . . . f . . . far better than all that gunge and grime rubbish they've been doing.'

'Och, it's still a crappy commercial. Thunder and lightnin' and all that. What does it *mean?*'

'I'm not so sure. It may be lousy c . . . c . . . creatively, but . . . but it's bound to have impact. And memorability. And it says moisturising s . . . strongly enough.'

'It's crap.'

'Well what,' Harry interrupted his partners, 'can we do about it, now we know about it?'

'We've no need to do anything,' Bill insisted, standing up and strolling restlessly around the room. He did not enjoy knowing what his competitors were up to. It was like cheating

at cards. When people cheat, he believed, they usually lose.
'It's crap. Forget it. Let Pendletons hang 'emselves with it.'
'That's not enough,' Harry urged.
'N . . . no. Harry's right. We ought to research it. The m . . . m . . . moisturising strategy, I mean. Then we can kill it at our presentation. We can't test their commercial, that would be too obvious. B . . . b . . . but we can test the c . . . concept.'
'We've not got the time.'
'Yes we have. We'll g . . . get Greg Hamilton to do it. I wanted to g . . . get him in on this pitch all along.'
'Well you'd better get on to him right away,' said Harry. It would cost another few thousand quid, but now he'd stitched up GOB, and had all but stitched up Pendletons, the business was virtually won.

Unsurprisingly, Messrs Gilbernetti, Orr and Burton found *Campaign*'s revelations more than a little dispiriting. Under the front page banner headline 'LARSONS £6M UP FOR GRABS' – a typical fifty per cent exaggeration as they knew from having seen Larsons' marketing plans – there was a story which included the following breathless Gail Hawkins' paragraphs:

> *Campaign* understands it will be a no-holds-barred three-way pitch, with incumbent Pendletons fighting hard to stave off hot competition from Adams Coventry McAndrew, and Gilbernetti, Orr and Burton.
> However Larsons Marketing Director, Peter Dalrymple, claimed it was 'just a review', and while implying Pendletons would keep the business, denied Gilbernetti, Orr and Burton were involved, adding that he had never even heard of them.

Irving Gilbernetti, who had been excitedly polishing his Eurekan idea for two days with a view to revealing it to his partners that afternoon, was distraught.
'Looks like your pal Digby has fucked us over real good,' he said as the three of them sat around the large dark made-to-measure walnut table, a remnant of Irving's mark I décor which had, due to its cost, survived the refurbishment and looked particularly ill at ease among Irving's mark II décor.

'I can't believe it. He wouldn't do that to me.' Hal Burton, drinking his third cup of tea and nibbling chocolate wholemeals, had now said the same thing about a dozen times, shuffling the words only slightly at each repetition.

'Thank goodness we didn't do all that redecoration.' James Orr was the only one of them able to glean some slight, perverse pleasure from the situation. GOB's lack of success consistently reinforced his conviction that all clients were perfidious pigs, and that only the very inexperienced and the very stupid could think otherwise.

'We can cancel the bits we agreed to go ahead with, I hope. The reception and so on. Can't we?'

'What about Greg Hamilton? We're seeing him tomorrow. What'll we say to him?' asked Hal.

'Cancel him too. Phone him now. He can't charge us for work he's not done. Can he?' James remained calm.

'I'm sure there's a mistake,' Hal insisted. 'Des Digby wouldn't do that. I can't believe it.'

Hal had phoned Larsons as soon as he had seen the news, and been told that Des Digby was out of the office until late afternoon. He had phoned *Campaign*, but Gail Hawkins had refused to expand upon her printed story. Now he phoned Greg Hamilton's office and cancelled their appointment for the following day.

James Orr twisted his gangly limbs uncomfortably in his chair, took off his thick spectacles and replaced them immediately. All three were silent, unable to think of what to do next. After a few minutes James spoke, in a dull monotone. 'I suppose I'd better tell you that our latest budget figures are projecting a £230,000 loss this year. And there's no way we can cut costs to save that.

'Even if we fired everyone we'd have to pay redundancies. I didn't tell you before, as I thought we might win Larsons. Technically we're bankrupt.'

Unusually, Ralph Isaacs found little to interest him in that morning's *Campaign*. Isaacs and Isaacs had won no accounts, lost no accounts, taken nobody over. One of their subsidiaries was on the short list for the peripatetic Albert-Culver business, another on the list for Sealink, which seemed to bob about almost as much. Boase Massimi Pollitt and Lowe Howard-Spink had both won sizeable slices of business, which irritated him a little, while Allen Brady and Marsh was re-pitching for one of its major clients: ABM was not having much luck lately, and he wondered what was going wrong there. In the gossip column there was a silly story about Johnny Heist, hinting not very subtly that he was about to leave Isaacs and Isaacs, which Ralph knew to be nonsense: J. Walter Thompson had tried to poach him, but Jonathan Forbes – on Ralph's instruction – had offered to install a sauna and sun-tanning bed in Johnny's home, which had swiftly persuaded him to stay put. There was a titbit about Gray Joliffe's book, *Wicked Willie*, being translated into Latin, for use in schools. There was yet another feature about yet another group of hot new agencies, with pictures of Robin Wight, Tim Delaney, Bill McAndrew and Ronnie Kirkwood – heaven knows (but Ralph didn't make the effort to find out) why Ronnie was there. And yet another supercilious article by Winston Fletcher which he couldn't be bothered to read; somebody should tell that guy that not all publicity is good publicity.

There didn't appear to be much in *The Financial Times* either – though he skimmed through Fiona McKuen's feature on global advertising, which mentioned Isaacs and Isaacs favourably three times – until his eye was caught by a snippet on the company news page. Fine Fare had made an agreed bid for Spilch Superstores, and, subject to shareholders' approval (which was expected), the acquisition would be completed on 15th November. After which the Spilch stores would trade under the Fine Fare banner, and the Spilch name would disappear.

So his cousin had been right. Though Ralph never admitted as much to anyone else, least of all to Stan, he was privately in awe of his cousin's business acumen. Stan too often lacked the courage of his convictions (a failing of which nobody could accuse Ralph), but his instincts were always good. He had sensed Spilch was a takeover prospect, and so it had proved. Which meant GOB must be deep in the mire. Ralph had suspected it when they refused to negotiate. He, too, had sensed that there was something fishy about Spilch but had, on this occasion, come to the wrong conclusion. Kelly could be told to stop chasing the business.

His phone warbled. 'Kelly's just told me Spilch have been taken over by Fine Fare,' Stan told him.

'I know, I know,' Ralph replied irritably, and slowly put down the receiver.

If GOB were going up the creek there might be some accounts left there which would be worth chasing. Crispins was still there, for one. Kelly must be put on the job immediately. To get the richest pickings, it was vital to be the first vulture on the scene.

VI
Interrogations

'Congratulations on being on the Larsons' short list. In *Campaign* this morning.'

'We seem to be on every list going. It's straining our resources a bit, too. We're all working twenty-five hours a day. Especially Mike and Bill. The rare occasions they get home their kids don't recognise them.'

'Just like Marvyn here. He always introduces himself when he gets home because his family forget who he is. You're not married, are you?'

'Me? No. Never met Miss Right. But hope springs eternal. My demands are quite simple. I just want someone who is young, beautiful, aristocratic, utterly obedient and very, very rich.'

And presumably rather boyish, thought Stan Isaacs, feeling sorry that Harry Adams felt it necessary to lie about his homosexuality, and forgetting that he himself had deliberately provoked the lie by inquiring about Harry's marital circumstances.

It was after six thirty, and they were sitting in Stan's office, next door to Ralph's, ostensibly having a drink, though none of them were drinking alcohol. Harry and Marvyn Gottlieb, Isaacs and Isaacs' Financial Director, were drinking Perrier, and Stan had poured himself a coffee from the small percolator that he kept permanently bubbling on his filing cabinet. Ralph had long gone home; not that he would have met Harry Adams, even had he still been at work.

'You're certainly doing well,' Stan dutifully flattered his guest. 'How do you get on so many new business lists?'

'You know the ad game as well as I do. Clients are like moths, drawn by the brightest flame around. Isaacs and Isaacs used to be the same. But no agency can keep burning brightly forever. That's the nature of the game.'

'And that's why you're here?' Marvyn Gottlieb queried, though it wasn't quite clear from his tone of voice whether he was asking or stating.

'I'm here because you invited me. We're not exactly hawking ACM round town.'

'Of course not.' Stan swiftly soothed Harry's pique. Marvyn was in too much of a hurry; he shouldn't have put on his Mr Nasty hat yet. 'I'm interested in what you said about Isaacs and Isaacs,' Stan continued. 'Why do you say we're burnt out?'

'Burnt out? Far from it. I didn't say that. But you're not a hot creative agency any more. You're too big. You're a business. A machine. An investment. But not an advertising agency.'

'We still win more creative awards than any other agency in the country.'

'We're talking about perceptions, not reality,' Harry insisted. 'Everyone knows you're still a great agency, if they think about it logically. But they don't think about it logically.'

'I'm not sure.' Stan had heard the argument Harry was propounding many times of late, and thought it simplistic. Conventional advertising wisdom has it that only small agencies could be truly creative, that big agencies suffocate in committees, in organisational and financial problems, become too greedy for profit, have too many large unimaginative clients, and so cease to create exciting advertising.

It was a cliché he believed Isaacs and Isaacs' own performance had empirically disproved. But most advertising people still stood by it.

'Well, it's very nice of you to come and see us,' said Marvyn, doing his damnedest to be warm and friendly, but patently uninterested in abstract discussions concerning agency structure about which, he had learned from experience, agency people natter on interminably, 'but we invited you over to see if there's any way we could do a deal between us.' Marvyn took very seriously the precept that time is money. He was a short, stocky man with large, brown owlish eyes, black crinkly hair, and a charming smile which he rarely smiled. Instead, his face was generally set in a gloomy, pained scowl. His ability to switch between fearsome scowl and lovable smile was indubitably a powerful weapon in his negotiating armoury.

'Really? I thought you'd asked me over because you liked the colour of my eyes.'

Once more Stan needed to intercede. Adams was apparently a prickly character, and Marvyn was far too impatient. These things take time. 'Obviously we're interested in seeing if there's any way we can get together,' Stan said. 'There's no contesting ACM is far and away the best young agency in town. And that makes you an exceptionally worthwhile acquisition, from our point of view. At Isaacs and Isaacs we've always been keen on buying talent.'

'Really? I thought you were more interested in buying businesses. You've bought some fairly talentless businesses in the past.'

'Sure we did. We bought businesses to grow bigger. Now we're big we need more good people. As many as we can get. To help us run the ship.' That, Stan hoped, should attract him.

'The difficulty,' Harry began his pre-calculated response, 'is that we're too new, too young, too small. We've only been going three years, and we'll only make about £300,000 pre-tax this year. That's a drop in the ocean to you. It's not worth you buying. Or us selling.'

Dead right, thought Marvyn. He could not think why Ralph and Stan were interested in ACM at this stage. It was a nice little agency, but little was the operative word.

'We'll pay a lot for talent. Tell me about your partners.'

Briefly, Harry ran through Bill McAndrew's and Mike Coventry's biographies. After leaving art school Bill had joined CDP where he had worked on Benson and Hedges – do you recall some of those lovely pure gold ads? – and on some of the early Heineken commercials, and on Fiat; then he'd moved to Wight Collins shortly after they started, but that turned out to be a mistake, because he was unable to work with Ron Collins and had been wondering where to go next when Harry had approached him. Now, at thirty-four his creativity was bursting into full flower, and ACM were scooping up creative gongs worldwide.

'He's difficult, but not too difficult,' Harry ended, 'so clients love him. As a manager he maybe doesn't delegate enough, but that's not such a terrible fault. And he's a physical fitness freak. Not my style, I can tell you. His only idiosyncracy is that he's recently been converted to Judaism. But I guess that would be no disadvantage at Isaacs and Isaacs.'

Stan pointedly ignored what might have been, but most probably was not intended to be, an anti-semitic remark. Like most Jews in business, he had long ago inured himself to such trivial instances of possible anti-semitism: it was simpler, and quicker, and probably wiser, to ignore them. (This was not a view his cousin Ralph shared.) 'And Mike Coventry?' Stan inquired.

Marvyn, who ought to have been listening, had opened a file of financial reports and was working through them, occasionally doing sums on his calculator and muttering inaudibly to himself.

After leaving the London School of Economics, Mike Coventry had spent a year in Africa with Oxfam, but the scale of the problems, and the hopelessness of the situation, had depressed and enervated him, and he had finally fallen ill – probably from despair, Harry believed. Once he had recovered, and in complete contrast, he joined Boase, Massimi, Pollitt, where he trained to be a planner under the legendary Stanley Pollitt – before Stanley died of overwork and over-indulgence celebrating Mrs Thatcher's victory in 1979. Without Stanley Pollitt, Mike had decided – incorrectly as it turned out – BMP would soon be in the doldrums. So he accepted the daunting task of setting up a planning department in Ted Bates when it was offered to him. But he didn't make much progress (all the American multinationals had found it hard to graft the British approach to planning on to their own systems) and he was ripe for the plucking when Harry approached him.

Harry then extolled Mike's inordinate enthusiasm for client-hunting – like a beagle with the scent of a myriad hares – and was about to describe his current balloon race with McCanns for the Thistelthwaite Jammes account but thought better of it. Isaacs and Isaacs were bound to have innumerable keen balloonists on their pay-roll, all of whom would immediately be ordered up, up and away to join the aerial dogfight if he revealed to Stan that Thistlethwaites' account was loose. 'Mike's great strength,' he said instead, 'is originality. He doesn't simply analyse the data and the figures. Anyone can do that. But Mike sees patterns in them. To him statistics create images. They bore me silly. They excite Mike. And the best thing about both Bill and Mike,' he added, 'is that they're both really nice guys. Great to work with, and honest as the day is long. Which is more than you can say for most people in this business. A lot more.'

Stan looked at his Rolex. It was now past seven thirty, and pitch dark outside.

Marvyn, sensing that the boring bit had finished, looked up from his calculations. 'What do you think your agency's worth?' he asked brusquely, as far too much time had already been wasted.

'I told you. We're not for sale.'

'So why did you come?'

Harry had gone there partly out of curiosity, to meet Stan Isaacs. He had hoped to meet Ralph, but knowing of Ralph's reclusive reputation had not expected that to be likely. And he had wanted to hear what they would have to say, which so far had been singularly little. Stan, of course, was a far more experienced negotiator than Harry.

Stan also knew that if ACM won Larsons, let alone any other business they might have in the pipeline, their profits would leap up next year, making them an even more delectable acquisition. 'You've not told us anything about yourself.'

'Me?' Harry elegantly crossed his Huntsman grey flannel-clad legs, tucked his Turnbull and Asser tie tidily into the double-breasted jacket, and adjusted his horn-rimmed spectacles: all specially and soberly chosen for the occasion. 'I just hold the purse-strings, keep the clients quiet, and whip Mike and Bill when it's necessary. Which isn't often. As I've said, I'm irrelevant, expendable.' He laughed.

Stan's office was more spartan than Ralph's, with no expensive modern paintings but with an array of house plants, perhaps thirty in all, creeping luxuriantly into every nook and cranny, lovingly tended by Stan and his secretary. The room was lit only by a desk light and a simple standard lamp, under which Marvyn was sitting so that he could continue to work at his figures. Although his eyes had grown accustomed to the dim light, Harry could hardly see Stan's face. Stan, in contrast, was seeing more clearly than of late, having given up his irritating contact lenses and returned to his old, comfortable rimless spectacles.

'This is only an idea,' Stan said, 'at this stage. But if we bought ACM and merged you with . . . with one of our other agencies, one of the big ones, so that together the merged agency would be one of . . . one of the top ten agencies in the country, would that interest you?'

Marvyn looked up, startled. What on earth was Stan talking about? They had not discussed the possibility of merging ACM with one of their other agencies beforehand; the meeting was to have been purely exploratory.

'What would be my title? I mean my job?' asked the irrelevant, expendable Harry immediately.

'Chairman. You'd be running it. The whole show.'

'What about Mike and Bill?'

'Bill would be Creative Director, that's certain. I'm not sure about Mike. We'd have to explore that.'

Harry's brain hopped and skipped like a computer testing the alternatives for a fit. Which of the Isaacs' agencies could Stan be talking about? It couldn't be . . . or could it? No. What about . . . ? Hardly. Who in hell could it be? None of them fitted.

'We'd have to find a place for Mike,' he said, not too forcefully.

'Of course we would. Of course we would. Anyway, I can take it that if everything else could be agreed, you'd be interested?'

'Well . . . yes, I would. I mean we would. Definitely. If everything else could be agreed, I mean.'

'That's good. Excellent. Could you send your latest balance sheet and this year's financial forecasts to Marvyn? In strictest confidence, of course,' Stan said, standing up. 'Hell, it's nearly eight o'clock! Can you find your own way out, Harry? Sorry to rush you. Don't forget to send the stuff to Marvyn. Just take the lift. Where's my coat?'

'Hey,' Marvyn whispered loudly as Harry left, 'what were you talking about? Who can we merge him with? We haven't got anyone who needs a merger.'

'Unless the Pendletons deal goes through, you schmuck. Which it will. Then folding ACM into them, as a reverse takeover, would be just what that old place needs.'

'But what about the existing Pendletons' management?'

'I'll miss the curtain for sure,' Stan said as he hurriedly put on his overcoat. 'She'll go spare again. Oh hell!'

'So why don't you want to see me any more?'

'I . . . I just don't. I wish you'd stop asking.'

Simon Booth and Jenny Sandford were sitting in Grape Little Idea, one of Covent Garden's many new wine bars. It was just after six thirty, and there were only a couple of other customers. Grape Little Idea was as dissimilar from The Quills as it was possible for two central London booze-peddling parlours to be. Indeed, it was everything that Wally and Molly, and Tom Nathan and his chums, vehemently despised. It was brightly lit by circular fluorescent tubes and flashing zig-zag neon lights; at one end of the bar was a video-projector which permanently ran pop-promo-videos at decibel levels which would have been acceptable to the Managing Director of Pierre Renoir Perfumes even if he were wearing ear-plugs; all the surfaces were pastel ochre and turquoise formica; the mirrors were phony art nouveau, and posters on the walls promoted such toothsome cocktails as The Leg Opener, The Brain Crusher, Bum-Bum-Bum, How About a Knee Trembler, and Suck It'n See. Simon was slowly sipping his second Old Tosspot, and Jenny had already nervously gulped down her second Dreadful Double Daiquiri. They had often met at Grape Little Idea in the early weeks of their courtship, but had since avoided it for fear of being seen together. Now it didn't seem to matter.

'But you can't suddenly decide you don't want to see me any more. Just like that. Without warning. You can't.'

'Why not? One partner always has to decide first. Then it comes as a bit of a surprise to the other, I suppose.'

'But . . . ' Simon searched for the right word. He wanted to say 'civilised' or 'well-behaved', or 'properly-educated' but all of them sounded too pompous for Jenny, 'but . . . well-mannered people, I mean adult people, don't just break off relationships. All of a sudden. With no explanation. It's not done.'

On the contrary, thought Jenny, that's exactly how it always was done at Woodbury Town Comprehensive School, even if not at Harrow. For her it always had been done that way and always would be. Discussions and post-mortems were embarrassing and pointless. A swift and certain cut was always cleanest. Conversations and explanations only made things messier, nastier. In any event, she had given him plenty of notice, if only he'd noticed. She now regretted having agreed to meet Simon that evening. She should have stuck by her instincts, and finished it with her brief statement on the phone. But she had wanted to behave correctly, like a properly-educated, well-behaved, civilised adult. And he had sounded so surprisingly dejected when she had told him that she had felt compelled to comply with his request for further explanation; a request she now found herself unable to meet.

'Can I have another drink?' she asked, uncertain if it was wise to get drunker, or stay longer, but anxious to anaesthetise her mind.

As she watched Simon go to the bar with apparent reluctance (he had never been the most generous of blokes), she felt a twinge of sadness at the dissolution of their relationship. He was tall, classy, well-dressed, intelligent and really quite nice: all the things she consciously wanted, ought to want. But he lacked magnetism. She knew Tom Nathan would never be a steady. He would see her when it suited him, when he fancied, which would not be often. She knew she was throwing herself back on to the singles market, without a regular date, condemning herself to going out with girlfriends hunting for men (but pretending otherwise), gossiping enviously about other girlfriends' boyfriends (but pretending otherwise), dressing up and making-up a bit too immodestly (but definitely pretending otherwise). She knew, as she looked at Simon's slim hips and long, elegant legs, that she would often lie alone in bed and wonder why on earth she had ended it. But she knew she had no choice. She no longer fancied him.

At the bar, as he watched the barman unhurriedly concoct their cocktails, Simon was angry, gloomy, bitter and confused. He, too, foresaw a return to the singles market, which was hateful and undignified. Making the first moves in any new relationship filled him with trepidation. The first invitation to go out, the first touch, the first kiss, the first screw: there were so many possible occasions for hurtful rebuttal. He was never relaxed with a prospective girlfriend until the preliminaries were over and the affair was well under way. He could never understand a girl's POV. Many chaps said they found the first kiss, the first screw especially exhilarating. Not Simon. He found them intimidating, uncomfortable, awkward, anything but fun. He envied enormously all those other males whom, he imagined, handled such events effortlessly.

The mistake he had made, he decided as he searched for his money, was taking her for granted. He had been convinced, without having analysed the matter too closely, that she had been crazy about him. Not an unreasonable belief, he still felt, in view of all that he represented to her. She was no beautiful heiress, nor deb of the year. Apart from her red hair, she wasn't much at all. So why was she ending it so abruptly? There are proper ways, and formalities, and rituals which must be observed before lovers split up . . . warning shots must be fired, notices posted. Just as there are proper ways and formalities and rituals which must be followed when clients and agencies split up. Warning shots must also be fired, notices must similarly be given. And, now he thought of it, neither Jenny nor Larsons knew how to behave like gentlemen, according to Queensberry Rules.

'So what happened when you visited that Reg Hampton?' she asked as he returned to their turquoise cubicle, whose bench seats and knee room had seemingly been designed for midget contortionists.

'Reg Hampton?'

'That market researcher you went to see.'

'Greg Hamilton.' Had she made such a mistake the week before he would have iced his response with sarcasm. Now he restrained himself. He wanted to question her further, but like her – if for different reasons – he thought it might be better to talk about something else. Perhaps in conversation he could rebuild the broken bridges, and persuade her to recant. 'He's a funny bloke. Not at all what I expected. Lovely offices though . . . A small modern block just off the King's Road; hidden behind some plane trees, but light and airy. You'd like it.'

'What's he like, then?' Jenny half-emptied her glass, breathing a sigh of relief that Simon had ceased his inquisition.

'Small. And chubby. And balding. With his few remaining strands of hair combed forward across his head, you know, to try and hide his baldness. With trousers a bit too short and a waistcoat a bit too small, undone and covered in cigarette ash. Not at all impressive. Not to look at.'

'Was he old?'

'About forty-five I'd think. With a slightly odd accent. Maybe he was American. Or maybe he's lived there. Or maybe he just puts it on.'

'So what did he say?'

'Well once he starts talking, he's magic. I was only there less than half an hour, and he grasped the whole thing. He's got a brain like a computer.'

'Did you play your trick?'

'Trick? What trick?'

'You know. You were going to get him to throw out Tom Nathan's campaign by doing the sample wrong somehow. Wasn't that it?'

'Oh that. I decided not to do it. Dirty tricks aren't my bag.'

'I'm glad.' Ever since Simon had told her of his plan to torpedo Tom Nathan's campaign the subject had obsessed and depressed her. She couldn't tell why, but she was certain Simon was not clever enough to mount such a scheme. He would get caught and probably fired. At the same time, Tom's campaign would be ruined, so he would be upset, and Pendletons would lose the Splashasoap account, and there would be more sackings, including her maybe, and all because Simon wanted to get his own back on Tom, like a schoolkid. Anyway, Simon had seen sense, thank goodness. She finished her third Dreadful Double Daiquiri and having had no lunch felt distinctly woozy.

'What did he say, then, that impressed you so much? The little fat man, I mean.'

'It was the questions he asked, his analysis of the problem. His main point – it's obvious when you think about it – was that there is no *logical* reason for using liquid soaps. So we've got to provide psychological, emotional reasons. That's why "gunge and grime go away" is so off-beam. There's nothing wrong with ordinary bar soaps. Housewives aren't going around grumbling about soap all the time. And Splashasoap isn't cheaper than bar soap, it's more expensive. So why should housewives use it? The answer is they don't. Not many of them. Unless we can give them what Hamilton calls a logico-psychological reason, they won't. A reason, that is, that's logical within a psychological framework? Do you follow?'

Grape Little Idea was crowding up. None of the customers looked more than twenty, and Simon was the only one wearing a suit. All the rest, boys and girls alike, were dressed in post-punk fashions: Sid Vicious and Johnny Rotten made socially acceptable. Compared to all the other girls present Jenny Sandford was, he thought, stunningly attractive, and he reached across and took her hand.

'Shall I get another round?' she asked, withdrawing her hand. 'You've bought three.'

'Do you want one?' he asked, conscious of her rejection.

'Not unless you do.'

'OK,' he said, 'I'll get it.'

She went off to the loo, while he fought his way to the bar through the noisy crowd that was now two or three deep, and by the time she returned two boys had stolen their cubicle.

'Excuse me,' Simon said politely but firmly, 'but those are our seats.'

'*Were* your seats, you mean. Now they're ours. Piss off.'

Both of them wore studded black leather jackets with huge epaulets, black jeans, high boots and had long unkempt hair. One had a small moustache, the other a stitched-up scar across his cheek beneath his left eye. Neither looked to Jenny like blokes to tussle with.

'You saw us sitting there,' Simon was saying 'you knew they were our seats.'

'And you pissed off so we took 'em. Now piss off again. Go back to Eton or wherever you come from, wanker.'

'Get off our seats!'

'It doesn't matter, Simon. Let's just finish our drinks and go.'

'If you don't piss off, wanker, I'll stuff your teeth right down your throat till they bite your cock off.'

'I said shift!'

Slowly, with studied concentration, the nearer of the leather jacket boys collected some sputum on his tongue and spat the blob of gob straight on to Simon's cheek. From then on Jenny watched the events unfold as if in a slow-motion movie, on a screen far away yet all around her.

Simon turned, the spit still on his face, carefully put the drinks he had been holding in Jenny's hands, then moved into the cubicle, grabbed one of the leather jackets with both fists, and started to tug its owner out of the seat.

Within seconds all was pandemonium. Both the leather jacket boys began punching at Simon's head, and his nose spurted blood, while he swung wide punches back at them, his long arms keeping them at bay. He landed a cutting thump on the moustached boy's right eye, which immediately began to bleed. Other customers crowded in and grabbed all three of them, pulling them apart; limbs and bodies jostled Jenny hither and thither, while she tried to stay upright and not spill the drinks. She was entangled in a jungle of arms and legs. But by the time the two big barmen arrived each of the three combatants had been pinioned by a strait-jacket of customers shouting, 'Cool it,' 'Relax,' 'Leave it.' One of Simon's eyes was swelling and growing darker, his nose still trickled blood. It had happened so quickly, so unpredictably that Jenny wondered fleetingly whether she might have been dreaming.

'Fuck off, the three of you. Don't come back. We don't want your type in here,' shouted the bigger of the two big barmen. 'If you start again I'll 'ave the rozzers here from Bow street double quick.'

The customers relaxed their grips, and the leather jacket boys pushed their way out, shouting 'wankers' and 'shitheads' at all and sundry, ferociously kicking the seats and table legs, and a girl's ankle, probably by mistake. She screamed five-letter abuse at them as they left.

Simon shook himself free and said, 'We'll just finish our drinks,' through his cut and swollen upper lip. 'We've paid for them, so they're ours.'

'You've got thirty seconds,' said the barman, shoving him with his shoulder towards the door, while Jenny stayed beside him and handed him his glass. His knuckles were puffing up and his right hand was bleeding a bit. He swallowed what little was left of his Old Tosspot in one gulp, then left the bar, which had instantly returned to its ebullient status quo as though nothing had happened.

Jenny had been frightened the boys would be waiting outside in ambush, but they had gone. 'We'd better get a taxi to a hospital,' she said, 'you may need stitches.'

'Rubbish.' His confident tone, once again reminiscent of Biggles, had returned. 'I boxed for Harrow and got a half-blue at Oxford. I'd have killed those layabouts if everyone hadn't stopped me. A good hiding's what they deserve.'

'Well, you'd better come home,' Jenny said, taking his puffy hand, 'and I'll clean up your wounds.' She felt the incident had sobered her up, but she was still a little unsteady. 'We'll get a cab and call in at Underwoods for some dressing. I've nowhere near enough at home.'

At about five o'clock in the morning he woke for the sixth or seventh time, having spent a restless, fitful night. The aches and pains were growing sharper all the time, despite the half-a-dozen analgesics he had swallowed.

They had already made love twice, and it had been tense and affectionate, like it used to be, so Jenny felt exhausted when he nudged her awake again.

'Sorry,' he whispered, 'I can't sleep.'

'Shall I get more Anadin?'

'It's not that. It's something else. How does Tom Nathan know about us?'

'What do you mean?' she asked, moving away from him as if for safety.

'Tom Nathan. Yesterday. He said he knew we'd been . . . going to bed together, and all that.'

What bastards men are to each other, she thought; what stupid competitive bastards.

'How does he know? Who could have told him?'

'God knows,' Jenny replied, and he noted the fury in her voice, 'but I don't. Go to sleep.'

Now he had angered her again, he thought. Oh hell!

It was just after six thirty, and Francis Kemp-Lewis, Dave Horrell and Bernie Barnstaple were in Chris Beaumont's office, together with Chris and Ronald Dark, Pendletons' Finance Director. They had been there since five o'clock and were not making much progress. At about six Chris had unlocked his drinks cupboard, in the hope that alcoholic lubrication would help their lucubration, but was now regretting having done so. Ron Dark, who was due to retire in a couple of years, was seemingly engaged in a serious race with Dave Horrell to see which of them could reach leglessness first. With thirty minutes gone Dave had established a commanding lead, but Ron was a class performer whose bibulous powers over long distances were never to be underestimated. Not taking part in the race were Francis Kemp-Lewis, cantering along on a Lowenbrau, Bernie Barnstaple on a Perrier, with Chris Beaumont on a weak whisky and soda, still unstarted.

Having failed to get much change out of either Dave or Bernie, Chris now turned his fire upon the Vicar. It was vital to break through soon, and once one of them gave ground it would be easy to defeat them all. 'We're getting nowhere,' Chris said, tapping the glass top of his desk irritably with his pen. 'We must make some savings. What about you, Francis? I can't believe everyone in the creative department's giving blood, sweat and tears, working their balls off night and day. I know they aren't. We all know they aren't. So who could you lose?'

Chris was sitting behind his Hepplewhite desk, the other four in an uncomfortable semi-circle facing him. Normally, he would have held an evening meeting with drinks at the other end of his office, on the low leather settees around the coffee table. But he did not want the meeting to be relaxed. He was consciously using his desk to emphasise, albeit so far without much success, his status. Unlike the others, he hadn't even taken off his jacket.

'Well, I've given it much thought,' Kemp-Lewis replied, 'yes, much thought. But there's no fat in the creative department at all. None at all, I'm afraid.'

'Frankly, Francis, I find that hard to accept,' Chris said, looking down the computerised staff list in front of him. 'You've forty-three in your department, two more than this time last year, and our turnover is down by seven per cent. What are they all doing?'

'In the creative department work isn't proportional to turnover. It may be so in the media department, or in accounts. But when it comes to creativity ... a copywriter could sweat for weeks merely to get an idea for a tiny trade ad. You can't get great ideas to order, you know, like sausages.'

'Not here you can't,' agreed Dave Horrell, loosening his rainbow-coloured tie, 'but you can at every other agency in London.'

'Rubbish! At Pendletons the creative department is as fast and professional as any. But creativity isn't short-order cooking,' the Vicar leapt to the defence of his team.

'It's academic. Bob Boyne's baying for blood. He wants thirty heads, served up to him on a platter. We know we're going to lose Pierre Renoir. Maybe Larsons too. And we're not even achieving Pendletons' target profitability now.' Chris forced himself to propound the argument he so much despised.

'But nobody achieves group targets. We all know that,' Ronald Dark said. He was a heavy, flat-faced, dull-eyed man who nowadays drank a great deal too much. Were he not soon to be retiring, Chris would have been forced to fire him. As it was Chris had told him to recruit his successor, with a view to retiring him early – a transparent plot which Ronald, who had no wish, as he described it, 'to be put out to grass like a worn-out stallion,' balked by ignoring.

'Whether or not others make target profitability is irrelevant. With major account losses in the offing we've got to take precautionary measures. Francis, you've got to cut six people. At least six.'

'Six! Quite impossible. It negates all our plans for rejuvenating the agency. We agreed it to be essential to devote more resources to creativity to improve our creative product. Boyne agreed that too. At the annual review. Now you're asking me to decimate the department. It's madness.' When he was in a corner, most of Francis Kemp-Lewis's ponderous pomposity evaporated, and he argued his case with vigour.

'I want six names.'

'Can't be done, Chris. We can't just turn turtle on our previous plans. We've told the clients, we've told the trade press, we've told everyone how we are investing in the creative department. We can't go back on all that. I'll resign first. Why don't you cut back the media department? Why have they been let off?'

'They haven't. But they've got fewer people than last year. You've got more.'

'That was our agreed strategy.'

'*Better* creative people, Francis. Better. Not more.'

'The two go hand-in-hand. They're two sides of the same coin. I can't get better people unless I can give them more time to do good work. And that means more manpower in the department.'

Chris knew, and accepted, the strength of much of the Vicar's argument. He too was convinced that it was essential to invest in the creative department, in order to rebuild Pendletons' creative reputation. But he knew Boyne would be unmoved by the argument; and he himself suspected the Vicar didn't drive his team as hard as he should.

'What about old Stokes and Maureen Carpenter?' Chris asked, looking again at the staff list. 'They've not done anything worth looking at in twenty years.'

'Stokes and Carpenter? You must be crazy. Marmaduke would go berserk. They've been working on that account for the last nine years and Marmaduke still thinks they're the hottest thing since sliced bread.'

'Anyone else want a top-up?' Ronald inquired, as he took his own and Dave Horrell's empty glasses to the drinks cupboard and mixed two more quintuple gins and tonics.

'If you must have anyone,' the Vicar said in a falsely conciliatory voice, 'I suppose it had better be Nathan and O'Reilly.'

'Nathan and O'Reilly? After the work they've done on Splashasoap? I thought they were our great white hopes?'

'That Splashasoap campaign is dreadful,' Bernie Barnstaple interpolated, seeing an opportunity to grind his favourite axe, 'it'll never get through the market research. Greg Hamilton will see to that, I'm sure.'

'They are slow, disobedient, arrogant and unco-operative,' said the Vicar, 'and they're new, so no clients would miss them. In fact, after the way Nathan behaved at last week's meeting, Runalong would say a few Hail Marys if he went.'

'Really? What happened?' Chris Beaumont, a client service man to his fingertips, was easily diverted by the implication that Runalong had been upset.

'It wasn't important. They turned down Nathan's latest campaign – I knew they would – and he argued and argued with them. Wouldn't stop. Frightfully childish, as well as being tedious. They made their objections plain as a pikestaff, but Nathan wouldn't give in. In the end I had to tell him to shut up. It was exceptionally embarrassing. In front of the client I mean. He and O'Reilly are so stubborn and conceited they're impossible to deal with. They think they're God's gift to creativity, and they're doing us a big favour working here.'

'Are they doing a new campaign?' Chris was still concerned about the client.

'I've put Stokes and Carpenter on to it. They'll knock out something Runalong will like. Leave it to them.'

Runalong may well like it, Chris thought, but it won't be very creative. Stokes and Carpenter were old hacks who produced dull but competent ads. However, now was not the time to prolong the Runalong debate.

'We couldn't possibly fire Nathan and O'Reilly until after the Splashasoap presentation,' said Chris.

'Why not?'

'Because . . . because Des Digby's taken a shine to them.'

'That shit! He would. He's their sort.'

'Why don't we all face it,' Dave Horrell suddenly and surprisingly interrupted, 'the Vicar doesn't like Nathan and O'Reilly because they're more creative than he is. Don't worry, Francis ol' bean, we all get old. Can't be helped in this business. Then the young 'uns fuck us over. That's the way it is in advertising.'

'I've got to go in a few minutes,' said Ronald, who was clearly losing – or winning – his leglessness race with Dave, depending upon which view you took of victory, 'but here's an idea that will shut Boyne up. What about firing all the cleaners? And sub-contracting to an outside company?'

'That's stupid,' Chris replied. 'We can't do that. Boyne would never fall for it. He's asked for names.'

'We'll give him names. How does he know who Elsie Brown is? She could be a top art director!'

'It won't save any money.'

'Boyne's not asked for money, he's asked for heads. We can offer him nineteen cleaners' heads. It'll cut the payroll. It'll move to the suppliers' budget he never looks at. It will save a little, too. I've got quotes from cleaning contractors, and they're cheaper.'

'We can't fire those lovely ol' biddies,' Dave Horrell was almost literally crying into his drinks. 'Some of them have worked here for years and years. They'll die if we fire 'em.'

'We're not a charity, you know,' Bernie Barnstaple pointed out primly, taking off his heavy specs and pointing them purposefully at Horrell.

'It's a stupid idea,' Chris said firmly. 'It will hardly make any difference to our total profitability. So what's the point?'

'It will confuse the issue, that's the point,' replied the wily Ronald, 'and we'll still need to fire another dozen or so, to make Boyne's thirty heads. And those will save money. But it won't be too painful, is what I'm saying.'

'Seems like a good solution to me,' said Bernie.

'But they'll die if we fire 'em. Doing our cleanin' is their lives, I tell you. It's what they live for, some of 'em. They come in every mornin' and drink their tea and bikkies and chat. It's all they live for.'

'We're not the welfare state.'

'Well,' Ronald stood up. 'If we got rid of the cleaners and each department fired three people, that's twenty-nine. If we add Maisie, the client service tea lady and put in a machine, that'll be thirty. I'll fire three from my department if all of you will.'

'I can only manage two. I've thought about it. My department's smaller than the others. Two's all I can do,' Bertie Barnstaple responded.

'Me too,'agreed Dave Horrell. 'Two's maximum. The most. But whadabout the cleaners? We can't just kill 'em. Can we?'

'That's three from finance, two from media, two from research. What about you, Francis?' Chris knew he was now winning. He was still uncertain about the cleaners, but it was a neat trick, which might well work. It was getting late, and he yearned to get over to Flora's. He wondered what her reaction to firing the old cleaners would be. In any event, opening the bar had proved a good idea after all. 'We need three people from creative to make the thirty, Francis. But I'm afraid I won't accept Nathan and O'Reilly. In my view they're the best young team we've got. We need some guts on the creative floor, people who'll fight for their work.'

'The implication being,' Francis said in a monotone, 'that I don't.'

'C'mon Vicar, toss three names into the hat and we can all go off to the pub. Any names'll do except the big Jew and the small Irish, 'cos Chris said he won't accept 'em. Quite right too. You only want 'em out 'cos they're more creative than you. You're always the same, Vicar, you're so predictable.' Dave Horrell nodded enthusiastically to show how profoundly he agreed with himself.

Francis Kemp-Lewis was still smarting from Dave Horrell's earlier insult, and was furious Chris Beaumont had not then interceded on his behalf. Horrell was drunk, but that was no excuse. In vino bloody veritas, no doubt. He stood up and walked to the door. 'You can have as many heads from the creative department as you bloody well want, since none of you seems to give a damn about the agency's creativity anyway. Prick as many off the list as you like. Including mine. I've had enough.'

' 'E'll be all right in the morning. 'S jus' a liddle creative tantrum, tha's all it is. 'E'll be all right,' Dave opined cheerfully as he left. 'Come on, let's go to the pub.'

Chris shuddered, and closed his eyes. Oh hell, he thought, oh hell!

It was just after six thirty, and Irving, James and Hal were once again sitting around their walnut boardroom table, waiting for the phone to ring.

'Are you quite sure it's plugged through?' James asked irritably for the third time. 'It might be ringing in another part of the building.'

'Sure, sure. It's plugged through. Anyway we'd hear wherever it rang.'

'Not necessarily. Not if the doors are closed. I've missed calls before that way,' James was insistent.

'It's plugged through here. Believe me.'

They were awaiting a call from Des Digby. He had been out of the office all day travelling, but his secretary had phoned Hal shortly after lunch to say that Mr Digby would call them from home, as soon as he got back, shortly after six, to explain the *Campaign* story. She had added that Mr Digby had asked her to say the story as printed was full of mistakes, and that everything was all right.

Their spirits had been greatly raised, but until they heard the message from Des himself they were wary of growing too optimistic lest their hopes be dashed again. Messages that came via secretaries get garbled, like Chinese whispers. Unable to concentrate, none of them did any real work. Following James's revelations, each of them knew that upon Des's phone call hung the stark difference between bankruptcy and light at the end of the tunnel. Even if they were still on the Larsons pitch list they might not win. But they would not know that for weeks yet, in which time anything could happen. Moreover if they were on the list they would *have* to win, no alternative was acceptable, no alternative would be tolerated, no alternative could even be considered.

The phone rang, the ting-a-ling of an old-fashioned bell. The three of them glanced at each other, and Hal picked up the receiver.

'Gilbernetti, Orr and Burton,' he enunciated briskly and efficiently.

'GOB?' replied a cheerful Cockney voice. '*Sunday Times* here. Copy for Crispins this Sunday. It should've been here by now.'

'I'm afraid the person you want has gone home. Can you call back in the morning?'

'Morning'll be too late. Is there anyone else I can talk to? About Crispins' copy?'

'Tomorrow's only Friday. Surely that'll be OK for Sunday?'

'We're doin' the make-up tonight. Copy should've been here yesterday by rights.'

'I'm sure it's under control, but I don't know anything about it myself.' Hal put his hand over the mouthpiece and explained what was going on to his partners.

'Shall I repeat last month's copy? We've got it standing. I can't wait till tomorrow.'

'You'll have to wait.'

'You'll miss the insertion, mate. And you'll still 'ave to pay. No skin off my nose. Copy should've been here by Wednesday, by rights.'

'Ring off,' James instructed Hal. 'Tell him we're waiting for an important international call and ring off.'

'He says we'll miss the insertion. Crispins would be wild if we did.'

'For this Sunday? Bullshit. They don't print till Saturday.'

'Who am I speakin' to anyway?' asked the voice.

'Hal Burton. And I've told you, we'll get you your copy tomorrow. First thing. Don't worry.'

'I'm not worried, Mr Burton. It's you as should be worried. It's you as is in the shit, old son. Shall I repeat your last or not?'

'No.'

'On your head be it. Don't blame me if a blank space appears.'

'Ring off, for God's sake,' James Orr repeated, wriggling in his chair. His partners were far too soft. No wonder nothing ever got done.

'I'll strangle that bitch Maureen if we miss the insertion,' Hal said as he put the phone down, 'with my bare hands.'

'It'll be OK,' Irving soothed him, 'Maureen's never missed an insertion yet.'

The telephone rang again almost immediately.

'Gilbernetti, Orr and Burton.'

'Is that the Putney Public Library?'

'No.'

'Why not?'

'How the hell do I know why not? You probably dialled the wrong number.'

'Ring off.'

'I'm sure I didn't.'

'I don't care whether you did or didn't, madam. This isn't the Putney Public Library.'

Although their central heating switched off on its time-clock at six forty-five, and the room was now cooling, tiny beads of sweat had broken out on Hal's forehead and at the bridge of his nose. He wiped them away with his shirt-cuff. Normally they would by now all have been drinking, Hal and James heavily, Irving less; but none of them felt like it. Hal wanted to be cold sober when he spoke to Des, to miss no subtlety of insinuation or innuendo; James and Irving felt that alcohol would aggravate rather than alleviate the tension.

'I told you we should have kept the receptionist to man the switchboard,' Hal said. 'It sounds so amateur, me answering the phone all the time. It'll sound amateur to Des when he finally comes through, you know what he's like.'

'Rubbish. Nobody has their switchboard operating at seven o'clock in the evening, not even J. Walter Thompson or Isaacs and Isaacs. And,' James Orr clinched the argument, 'we'd have had to pay her overtime.'

To pass the time Irving had spent the afternoon tinkering with his Splashasoap campaign, fiddling with the designs, tickling the script, hopeful that he would now be able to present it to his colleagues the next day, more or less as originally planned but twenty-four hours late. James had sat at his desk reading *The Economist, Business Week* and catching up with some trade magazines; a luxury, he muttered to himself, he rarely allowed himself at work; such reading was for train journeys and weekends (which is why it was always behindhand).

Hal had slipped out to a sauna and massage parlour he frequented, in Dover Street, in the hope that an invigorating sweat followed by the ministrations of the parlour's cheerful but exceedingly rude masseuse would bring him relaxation. They didn't.

Once again the telephone rang and Hal answered it officiously.

'Is Irving there?' It was Rebecca Gilbernetti. 'Is that you, Hal?'

'Yes. We're waiting for a call from Des Digby at Larsons. Do you want to speak to Irving?'

'How's Joan? Is she recovering?'

'Oh she's recovering fine. She's a brave girl. I'm proud of her. Mastectomy's a terrible thing. But the prognosis is good these days.'

'I'm hoping to find time to visit her. It's the children make it so difficult.'

'She'd love you to. If you can find the time.' Hal was well aware that Joan and Rebecca did not get on well. Rebecca was a dowdy woman, charmless and intense, with no sense of humour or sense of clothes. Evenings out with the Gilbernettis, in the early days, had been torture.

'Well, give her my love when you next visit her.'

'I'm hoping to get to the hospital tonight. If only Des Digby would ring. Here, I'll pass you to Irving.'

'Hurry up,' said Irving as he took the phone, 'we're expecting Des Digby on this line any minute. He's an hour late already.'

At that moment the telephone rang in the next door office. 'Maybe that's him.' James jumped from his chair. 'Hal, run and get it. Quick. Before he rings off.'

They both dashed into the next office, but reached the telephone too late.

Meanwhile Irving, oblivious of their fruitless chase, was answering his wife's inquiry as to exactly when he would be home as she was, for a small family treat, cooking roast beef and Yorkshire pudding and wanted it timed to precision.

'It was your wife's bloody fault.' James could scarcely restrain his anger as he re-entered the room. 'We missed him!

He won't ring back now, it's after seven. What did she want that was so bloody urgent anyway?'

'Nothing much.' Irving apologised. He had been as anxious to hear from Des as any of them. 'Just wanted to know when I'd be home.'

'Checking up on you in other words. Checking up on you! How can we run a business with neurotic wives? Anyway, let's phone Des at home. I can't bear to wait till tomorrow. I won't sleep.'

'I'd sooner not. He won't like it. You know what he's like. He may be off with some bird.' Hal plumped himself down heavily in his chair. 'If he'd wanted us to phone him he would have said so. He may not even be calling from home.'

'I thought his secretary said he'd be home by six.'

That's what he told her. Doesn't mean a thing. Just means he thought he'd be somewhere he could telephone us from at six. Maybe in a pub, maybe in a floozie's joint. Who knows?'

'I'm sorry, guys. About Beccy's call, I mean. She'd never have done it if she'd known, I can promise you. Never.'

'Well, it's too late now,' said James glancing at his Longines, 'it's twenty past seven. He won't call back now. And we can't hang around all night.'

'Another ten minutes?' Irving suggested.

'Forget it. It'll be all the same in the morning. His secretary said everything's OK. Let's go.'

They collected their coats, Irving put on his Russian fur hat, and James sped through the small building methodically pulling out the plugs and switching off the lights, cursing those who had left them on as he did so.

After Hal had switched on the overnight burglar alarm and turned his key in the mortice lock, they heard a telephone start to ring somewhere back inside the building, but it only rang four or five times

'Oh hell,' Hal mumbled, 'oh hell!'

'I didn't sleep much last night.'

'Oh. Was it something you ate?'

It was just after eight thirty, and Des Digby was sitting across the desk from Peter Dalrymple, having been summoned to arrive at the office for an early meeting. The simple, metallic desk was bare but for a small, folded piece of paper. Peter prided himself on never leaving work out overnight.

'No, nothing I ate. I've decided the best thing, the only thing, is to show you the letter and hear your reaction.'

Des gleaned from Dalrymple's voice that something was seriously amiss. 'I'm afraid I've no idea what you're talking about . . . sir.'

'This,' Peter tossed the folded paper across his desk. 'You'd better read it.'

They sat in silence for a couple of minutes while Des absorbed the contents of the anonymous missive. His worst fears had been confirmed. He had known all along it was stupid to go to the Vanderbilt that night. Hal should never have used his real name.

'I suppose I should say that you've no need to say anything if you do not wish to.'

He's been watching too many police serials on telly, Des thought. But nonetheless he felt his stomach heaving, as though he might be going to retch. It was as well he had eaten no breakfast. 'It's lies, of course, sir. Complete lies. I'm trying to think why anyone would have sent it.'

'Why would they? If it's untrue?'

'I can't think, I honestly can't think.'

From the start, and in accordance with his inquisitorial plan, Peter Dalrymple had fixed his eyes on Digby's face, watching for any flicker of a falter, any glimmer of guilt. 'Why haven't you let me meet this Gilbernetti, Orr and Burton agency of yours?'

'I've not stopped you, sir. Well, I've not meant to. I've just tried to save your time. I told you, I inspected them myself and thought they were excellent.'

'Did you go out with this chap Burton afterwards?'

'Yes. We went to dinner at an extremely cheap Italian restaurant called Casa Roma. I doubt if the bill came to more than thirty quid. Hal Burton's probably got the American

Express chit if you want to see it, I expect. And the waiters would remember us. We were the last to leave.'

'Last to leave?'

'I told you Hal Burton and I worked at Beechams together, ages ago. And we've hardly seen each other since. So we reminisced, strolled down memory lane and so on. I think we finished with a couple of armagnacs and left around midnight. If I remember right.'

'Then?'

'Then Hal Burton went home and I took a taxi to the hotel. The Tara. You can check on that too if you like.' That, thought Des, was his first bluff. But he couldn't see old Dalrymple checking, and discovering he had returned to the hotel around three a.m. with the luscious Vera and slipped the night porter fifteen quid to let her stay the night.

'Have you seen Hal Burton on any other occasion?'

'Not for ... eighteen months at least.'

'Not at all?'

'No.'

'Did you ever go to a night club with him? When you were younger I mean?'

'Don't be stupid, sir. I never go to night clubs. Not like the Vanderbilt.'

'You've heard of the Vanderbilt, then?'

'Everybody's heard of the Vanderbilt.' It was a small slip, and Des swallowed drily.

'I haven't. Or rather hadn't.'

'Well you, sir, aren't ... in London much. You've never worked in London. And you don't mix in marketing circles much.'

'Marketing circles go to the Vanderbilt?'

'I've not the least idea. I'm sure some do. I understand the Japs like that sort of thing.'

As far as Peter could see, Digby had revealed no indication of guilt whatsoever. Even his knowledge of the Vanderbilt seemed to Peter to confirm his innocence: had he been lying he would doubtless have denied having heard of it.

'How would you feel if, in light of all this, I suggest we remove Gilbernetti, Orr and Burton from our short list, and substitute another agency? Or if it's too late, maybe we would just consider the other two.' It was Peter's forensic coup de grâce, and he watched Digby especially closely.

Des thought for several seconds before answering. 'I think it would be a pity, sir, because they're a good agency. So it would be our loss. And there certainly isn't time to brief another agency, so we would have to choose between Pendletons and ACM. But despite all that I think it would be better to strike them off the list. Because, after all, you probably won't be able to judge them fairly, hard as you'll try. And I'm not sure I would want them to win the business either. It would smell. Even though it's all untrue.'

There was another silence, while the older man stared ahead of himself, as if in a trance, now not seeing Des Digby's face upon which he had concentrated so fixedly for the previous fifteen minutes.

'Have you any other questions, sir?'

'No, thank you. If we do reject GOB' – Peter hated the acronym as he said it – 'we ought to pay them a small honorarium. Something to cover their costs so far. Now, I've got a meeting with the Chairman in five minutes, so I'd better get myself ready.'

'Mr Burton's on the line for you,' his secretary told Des as, utterly drained and exhausted, he arrived back at his desk at five to nine. His head thudded as though he had a violent hangover.

'Say I'm out. Say I'll be out all day. I don't want to talk to him. Or anyone. Oh hell,' he muttered, 'oh hell!'

VII
Confrontations

'That'll be ninety-two pence.'

Two pence more than Tesco!

Simon Booth pushed his swollen hand into his Harris tweed pocket and painfully extracted a one pound coin. The Boots cashier dropped the Splashasoap pack into his Tesco bag for him, and he clumsily picked up his change. He wondered if she wondered why he was wearing dark glasses on a rainy day in October, restrained himself from smiling a friendly smile because smiling hurt, and exited through the curtain of hot air.

He had decided during the night to play truant from work rather than face the inevitable questions, quips and sarcasm. He had telephoned Flora Thompson and more or less truthfully told her he wasn't feeling too well, and that instead of coming into the agency he intended carrying out a Splashasoap store-check. There was nothing, he added, that needed to be done urgently: everything could wait till Monday.

'Good idea. We can incorporate your store-check into the presentation. It'll show we're keeping close to the heart of the market,' Flora responded, adding a touch unrealistically, 'see if you can interview some supermarket managers on your travels. Ask them how they think it's selling, and its prospects and so on. You know the kind of thing. Have a good weekend. Hope you'll feel better by Monday.'

Boots was Simon's fourth port of call. He had previously visited Tesco, Fine Fare, and a small independent chemist. He had so far failed to make contact with a single store manager, not that he had tried too hard. Without a prior appointment it was all but impossible to get through to store managers at the best of times, and this was hardly the best of times. Flora Thompson, of course, was unaware of the situation. But your average supermarket manager, Simon felt reasonably certain, would be surprised to be interviewed by an advertising executive wearing dark glasses, with swollen lips, and one hand heavily bandaged and the other in sticky plaster. Even the Pakistani chemist, who could normally be expected to lack the *folie de grandeur* of a supermarket manager, had taken one quick peek from behind his dispensary and sent his counter assistant back with the message that he was far too busy with prescriptions to discuss Splashasoap this morning. When the sales assistant in Boots had told him that the manager was tied up, without even bothering to check, it was clear that his quest for a store manager to interview was unlikely to bear fruit. Simon decided to desist.

Anyway, he felt the endeavour to be futile. Store managers always seemed surprisingly ill-informed, or maybe unwilling to be informative, about the sales of goods in their stores. On previous outings, accompanied by clients' Sales Managers and with prior appointments properly made, the most precise pronouncements he had ever extracted from managers were either 'It's going quite well,' or much more often, 'It's not going too well at all. It's a bit slow/it seems to be sticking.' These less-than-scientifically-exact communiqués, Simon felt, added little to the sum of human knowledge.

Instead he was dutifully, if awkwardly because of the bandage, recording on a small pad the number of packs of each variety of Splashasoap he found on the shelves (Splashasoap being available in two perfumes: lemon, which smelt quite like lemon, and pine, which smelt quite like mildew); the shelf space occupied; the price; the competitors available and their prices; the neighbouring products; and whether or not any of Splashasoap's display materials were being used. (Each year Pendletons designed, and Larsons got printed, a vast quantity of showcards, shelf-strips, pack-crowners and the like, none of which, Simon suspected, ever saw the light of day. Despite which both Larsons and Pendletons put great store by these display items, the production of which was one of Simon's least favourite chores.)

At every retailer he visited he bought a pack of Splashasoap, partly because he felt uncomfortable entering and leaving shops without making a purchase and partly out of loyalty to Larsons and Pendletons: each purchase did its little bit to increase sales. As the plastic bag which he had picked up at his first shop grew increasingly bulbous its weight increasingly hurt his lacerated fingers, but he kept up his lone sales drive without flinching.

Before making each purchase Simon hung around the Splashasoap section for a while in the hope of seeing a real customer make a purchase. The odds against this happening, had he known it, were long: the average shop sold only 9.3 Splashasoap packs per week, and most of those on Saturdays. But to his joy and delight, at Sainsbury's, the eleventh of his intended twelve calls, as he approached the toiletries section he saw, he actually saw, an attractive young woman, a bleached blonde with spindly high heels ('housewife, aged twenty-five to thirty-four, probably C2 social class' he mentally noted) select a lemon perfume pack from the shelf and toss it into her trolley.

Simon felt a tremor of suppressed excitement. He was as gleeful as if it were a personal triumph. Now the event called for executive action. It was an opportunity for first-hand market research: a realistic in-store purchase, not a simulated, hypothetical 'would you buy this product if . . . ' questionnaire interview. Here was a housewife, probably C2, who chose to buy Splashasoap of her own volition, with her own money. Why did she buy it? What persuaded her? Was it the advertising? What did she think of the commercial? Was it a repeat purchase, or was it her first trial? What was her opinion of the pack? Of the name? Did she know it was made by Larsons? Did she think it was expensive? Or not really? Would she use it in the kitchen only? Or in the bathroom as well? What was her basic POV? Did she . . . would she . . . had she . . . the questions spun through Simon's mind as he traipsed behind her, wondering whether or not he dare speak to her, as she filled her trolley with a cornucopia of goods and goodies.

'Excuse me,' he said finally as they reached the checkout together, 'Do you mind if I ask you a few questions – confidentially of course?'

The woman had been uncomfortably conscious for some time that Simon was silently pursuing her around the store, dogging her footsteps, doing no shopping. In his excitement he had neglected even to pick up his regulation Splashasoap pack. 'Are you the store detective?'

'Oh no. I just want to ask you a few things.'

The woman examined Simon intently, as though he was a joint of meat whose sell-by date had passed. She scrutinised his sunglasses, and the purple eye they failed to hide, she scrutinised his swollen lips and bandaged hands. He was, she concluded, clearly some kind of villain. True enough, he didn't look like one or sound like one. But you could never tell these days. Not even in Sainsbury's. No doubt he intended to lure her off somewhere, with his posh voice and smart clothes. Starting out in Sainsbury's was the ideal cover. No one would ever suspect someone they met in Sainsbury's.

'Help!' she screamed, leaving her trolley and rushing to the cashier, 'Help! That bloke's after me! Look at him! The one in the dark glasses.'

As if from nowhere, a store detective appeared at Simon's side. Having spotted Simon lurking behind the woman he had been following the two of them, making an unlikely ménage à trois, for several minutes. 'Excuse me, sir,' he said politely but intimidatingly and loudly enough for other customers quickly to gather round, 'but can you tell me what you've been doing in the store? I see you've not been shopping,' he added, pointing at Simon's empty basket.

'I've . . . I'm carrying out some market research.'

'On behalf of who, sir, may I ask?'

'On behalf of . . . my firm. You won't have heard of them. Pendletons. Have you heard of them?'

The store detective declined to betray his ignorance of the sixth largest advertising agency in the world. Behind him the blonde woman was glaring at Simon, convinced he was a rapist and keen to re-enter the fray.

'Do you have the store manager's permission to carry out this, er, market research of yours?'

'I'm afraid not.'

'You should've heard the things he said to me!' the woman interrupted.

'I didn't say anything.'

'Liar! You tried to ask me confidential questions.'

'Wait a minute. I saw you speak to the lady myself, sir. Did he say anything obscene to you, madam? Make improper suggestions?'

'Well . . . not really . . . He was leading up to it. Any woman could tell he was. From his voice, I could tell.'

'Excuse me, sir,' the detective said, turning his attention to Simon again, 'can I see what you have in that Tesco bag?' He uttered the word 'Tesco' as though it were a blasphemy. Its presence in Sainsbury's clearly incensed him.

'Nothing,' Simon answered hopelessly, 'only some Splashasoap I've been buying in other shops.'

Opening the distasteful plastic bag the detective observed the Splashasoap packs, five of lemon fragrance, five of pine. 'I think you'd better accompany me to the office, sir.'

'Can't I come?' asked the woman. It was she, after all, who had caught him.

'If you wish, madam. But it looks like a routine case of shoplifting to me. If he didn't make any obscene remarks, that is.'

'He was going to. I told you. He was getting ready. I'm coming too.'

'If you insist, madam. This way.'

The store detective cut through the small group of silent customers which had gathered around them, keeping Simon close by him, and followed by the young woman. Sickened though he felt, Simon was relieved that he was not at all frightened. He knew that as soon as they reached the office, and made a few telephone calls, everything would swiftly be sorted out. And while he did not think he had kept every receipt for the Splashasoaps he had bought, he was certain most of them were in the bottom of the Tesco bag.

It took just twenty minutes to check the receipts and get through to Flora Thompson ('Yes, she's a director of the agency,' Pendletons switchboard confirmed) after which the detective and the store manager apologised to Simon, pointing out that his behaviour had been a trifle suspicious, and that he ought not to have tried to accost one of their customers on their premises. The customer concerned was far from convinced by the evidence and explanations offered to her, and left the store certain that Simon had used his posh gift of the gab to talk himself out of trouble and get away with it. 'Just look at him,' she said as her parting shot, 'does he look like a respectable advertiser?'

Ironically, it did not once occur to Simon, as it would certainly have occurred to Tom Nathan, that wandering around the high streets collecting not very useful information was an odd occupation for an ex-Harrovian ex-Oxonian. Far from it. The activity was sufficient unto itself. The contretemps with the high-heeled woman had merely been an unfortunate diversion.

As Flora Thompson had predicted, his store-check would impress Larsons with Pendletons' – and particularly with Simon's – enthusiasm, drive and commitment. Simon had not been in advertising sufficiently long to realise that the data he had so diligently collected, and that he would soon be presenting portentously to Larsons, was of no use to man or beast. The sample of stores he had visited was too small and unrepresentative to justify any but the most trite of conclusions. More accurate, more comprehensive data covering the same ground in far greater depth was regularly purchased by Larsons from two market research organisations. Had he succeeded in carrying out his interview with the bleached blonde housewife it would have been worse than worthless: it would have been misleading. He would have believed her opinions to be typical instead of being – as they so noisily proved to be – entirely personal.

As Simon reached the nearby multi-storey car park and slowly and cautiously spiralled his way down to ground level he wished that he were driving back to Jenny's. He wanted to tell her about the day's events. But that morning she had insisted – despite the previous night's apparent change of heart – that she had not revised her decision, and she was sorry, but it was still all over.

His gloom was slightly alleviated by the knowledge that his store-check had, in general, been a handsome success. A little editing, and he would be able to turn it into a thorough and professional report. Peter Dalrymple would know, though Simon didn't, that nobody would ever do anything with the information; Des Digby would probably know it; Chris Beaumont and Bernie Barnstaple indubitably knew it. Yet all of them, when the time came, would slap Simon on the back and congratulate him. They were convinced – without ever having analysed the matter too closely – that store-checking is a ritual which every aspirant advertising man must undergo, like square-bashing in the army, as part of his basic training.

The telephone was warbling as Harry Adams entered his office at just after nine a.m. Its pitch proclaimed it to be an internal, rather than external, call.

'Hallo?'

'Mr Adams?' It sounded like one of the secretaries in the media department.

'Yes.'

'I've someone on the line for you. It's come through straight to my office. He won't give his name but says you know him. He sounds Irish.'

Harry hesitated. 'OK. Put him through.'

'Harry?'

'I said never to phone me at work.' It was more than a week since they had spent the evening together and Harry – with admirable self-restraint he felt – had stopped himself from telephoning Paul, intensely though he had yearned to do so on many occasions. It was a relationship which could lead only to complexities and problems. Never mix business with lascivious pleasure, and never have affairs with boys in advertising. Those had been his guiding precepts over the years, and they had served him well. The evening with Paul had been an inadvertent, momentary – and delicious – slip, not to be repeated.

'I must talk to you. Not about . . . us. It's about the things going on here. At Pendletons. Awful things, An' it's because of Splashasoap.'

'Splashasoap?'

'Can we meet tonight? In The Queensbury? Or your place? It won't take long.' Paul had been hurt by Harry's failure to contact him. It had been such a great evening he was astonished that Harry had not bothered to follow it up. But such things happen. That was not why he was phoning.

Harry paused. 'You'd better come to my place,' he said reluctantly. 'About seven o'clock. Be on time, as I've a dinner at eight,' he lied. 'Do you know the address?'

'Sure.'

'Seven o'clock, then.'

Harry hated being rushed into things as soon as he arrived at the office. That was why he preferred to arrive early. He liked to settle himself in before the hubbub of the day began. He removed his Dior jacket, reclined in his Eames chair, put on his azure-framed spectacles and – still wondering what on earth Paul O'Reilly wanted – skimmed through *The Times*. Isaacs and Isaacs shares were down three pence. He wondered why. He also wondered whether, if the deal went ahead, Isaacs would make their offer in shares or in cash. And he wondered what Mike and Bill thought about the deal, which he had outlined to them briefly on the telephone after leaving Isaacs and Isaacs' offices. Neither had sounded too enthusiastic, but then neither of them had much understanding of takeovers and mergers, and viewed them with notable suspicion. He was still reading the paper, glancing down the letters page, when Mike Coventry came in.

Mike was agitated, his long, gangly limbs all but quivering. 'I hardly s...s...slept last n...n...n...night,' he stammered.

'What's the problem?' Harry inquired from behind his newspaper.

'Is B...B...Bill in?'

'No. He's editing the Brite Bites commercial.'

'Good.' Mike had decided he did not want to involve Bill in the matter. Not yet at least.

'What's the problem?' Harry repeated, folding up his newspaper. 'Let's get Janet to fetch some coffee.'

'N...no. It's this.' Mike threw a sheet of paper into Harry's lap, and continued, 'Janet f...f...found it yesterday evening. B...B...Behind her filing cabinet, where it had s...s...slipped.'

Harry recognised it instantly. It was an early draft of the anonymous note he had sent to Peter Dalrymple. He had suspected, while clearing up after his midnight typing vigil, that he had lost one of the copies; but his search for it had proved fruitless. 'So?' he said firmly.

'It's yours? Isn't it? You d...did it, didn't you?'

'Yes.' There was no point in lying. Bill McAndrew must have mentioned D'Arcy Degavino's telephone call to Mike.

'I think it's d...d...disgraceful. D...despicable.' Mike had been brooding about it throughout the night, and rehearsed innumerable derogatory adjectives in his mind.

'Why?'

Mike was, for a moment, stunned into silence. It had not occurred to him that Harry would not be contrite. 'B... because it's...appalling. Immoral. It's...despicable.'

'I can't see why. We want to win the Splashasoap account, don't we?'

'W...we want to win it fair. On the b...b...basis of our p...presentation. Not by underhand ch...cheating.'

'Rubbish, Mike. Rubbish! This is business, not cricket. It's advertising, not Oxfam. There are no rules, no correct forms of gentlemanly behaviour. We're all in it to win. Us, GOB, the Isaacs cousins, all of us.'

Mike was stupefied. He wanted to win as much as Harry or anybody else. But not if it meant crawling in the gutter. 'S...so if it helped us to win you'd have s...s...somebody blow our c...competitors' knee caps off? Or...do it yourself, perhaps?'

'Not at all. That's breaking the law. I don't break the law. Sending anonymous – but truthful – letters isn't breaking the law. Why shouldn't Dalrymple know about the skulduggery Des Digby gets up to?'

'F...f...fine. If you feel that strongly why d...d... didn't you s...s...sign the letter?'

Harry looked at his young colleague with a mixture of anger and affection. Harry had, he thought a bit bitterly, rather too much experience of what sorts of behaviour were, and were not, socially acceptable. He had acquired the knowledge all too painfully. Mike was so naïve, so silly. 'I thought of signing it. If we hadn't been competing for Splashasoap I might have done. But we are, so I couldn't.'

'I d . . . don't see why not.'

'Because then Des Digby would have made sure we'd be thrown off the pitch list. So we'd have lost. And GOB would probably win, without us competing. I couldn't sign it. But not because I'm ashamed of it.'

'You must be! I can't b . . . believe what you're saying!'

'Look, Mike. What is and what isn't acceptable behaviour when you're going after a big contract isn't written down anywhere. There's no published code of ethics. There are no rules and regulations. So there are no rules and regulations to break. And I've not broken any.'

'I th . . . think it stinks.'

'I know you do. Because you've got scruples of your own, notional rules of good behaviour, of what is and isn't right. But they're your rules. Not everybody shares them. I don't, for one. And Des Digby doesn't, that's for certain.'

'B . . . because other people behave like sh . . . sh . . . shits doesn't mean we have to.'

'Why should we fight with one arm tied behind our back?'

'That's not what I'm s . . . s . . . saying. I'm saying we shouldn't carve up our opponents with knives. That's not c . . . competition. That's hooliganism.'

'The difference between us, Mike, is you're more fascinated in the game than in winning. Like most British businessmen. That's why we're so hopeless at business. Americans, French, Germans – let alone Italians or Spanish – would have sent that letter without a moment's hesitation.'

'Well, I w . . . want to withdraw. I d . . . don't want to go ahead with the p . . . p . . . pitch. And when I tell B . . . B . . . Bill, I know he'll agree. We don't want to w . . . win that way.'

'For God's sake, Mike!' For the first time Harry's voice was crisp with anger. 'Don't talk such crap. There's no inherent difference in winning because Bill McAndrew is a million times more talented than Gilbernetti, or that old second-rater at Pendletons, than because I wrote the note. Bill was born talented and clever. So were you. They weren't. What's so ethical about that?'

'That's the w . . . w . . . way the game is played.'

'Exactly! You think it's a game. It isn't. It's life. Games were invented to reflect life. Not the other way round. It's not a game. And we're not playing. It's deadly serious. People's lives and livelihoods depend on it. Our lives and livelihoods. I didn't break the law. I didn't do anything wrong. And we're not withdrawing!'

Mike Coventry slouched into his most characteristic position, his elbow resting on his knee, his head in his hand, and stared at the floor. 'Let's see what Bill says,' he said sullenly. 'If he agrees with you, I'll accept the verdict.'

'Why should I?'

'Don't you feel you owe Pendletons anything? At all?'

'My dear Chris! Do you not realise that I have been well aware, this last year, of the pressure on me? Of the criticisms? Of what was going on behind my back? Do you think I'm stupid as well as – by your lights – uncreative?'

'Nothing's been going on behind your back, Francis. Nothing.'

'Who are you trying to fool? I've been struggling to rebuild this agency's creative reputation and what backing have you given me? None. It's been clear to a blind man you want me out. Everyone here wants me out. So I'm going. You should be delighted, overjoyed, grateful. Instead of quarrelling about it. I don't understand you, Christopher, truly not.'

Early the morning after Francis Kemp-Lewis's disconcerting resignation Chris Beaumont had flown off to a Pendleton's European management conference in Madrid. In the dull lulls accompanying such fascinating sessions as Multi-Lingual Creativity, Harmonising Cross-Frontier Strategic Planning, Keeping International Clients Happy, and Europe: Pendletons Power-Plus Profit Centre, Chris Beaumont had repeatedly considered phoning Francis. But he had come to the conclusion, like Dave Horrell, that the Vicar's resignation was a temporary tantrum, and one he would probably prefer to forget. On arriving back in London Chris had soon found this supposition to be wrong.

Now he was faced with a dilemma. The Vicar's assessment of the situation was broadly accurate. Chris Beaumont and the rest of Pendletons' senior management felt Francis Kemp-Lewis to be a nice man, a kindly man, a hardworking, conscientious, intelligent man: but they wanted him out. They blamed him, by no means altogether justly, for Pendletons' uninspired creativity and uninspiring creative reputation. Chris knew the problem lay deeper, embedded in Pendletons' traditions and in its adherence to the 3-S philosophy. But, despite the Vicar's suspicions to the contrary, Chris had never discussed the issue with any of Pendletons' other directors. He had not thought the time yet ripe for firing the Vicar, and he could not be party to criticisms of the agency's Creative Director until he was ready to take action.

If the time was not ripe for his sacking, it was even less ripe for his resignation. With the Splashasoap repitch in the offing, with the restructuring of the creative department in progress, with employee morale low, and without a replacement in sight, the peremptory departure of the Vicar would be another blow to the agency's recovery. Worst of all, it would unsettle Marmaduke Confectionery. Chris had been striving to persuade Marmaduke to switch to Pendletons some of the brands currently handled by competitive agencies – Marmaduke employed four agencies and kept each on its toes by switching brands between them, to punish and reward – and the high esteem in which the confectionery company held the Vicar was one of the most effective weapons in Chris's persuasive armoury.

'Everyone recognises the contribution you've been making,' Chris said, 'getting the creative department up to scratch again. Everyone isn't against you. You've got your critics, like everyone else. Like me, like Horrell, like everyone. That's part of what we get paid for. You're being paranoid.'

'Maybe I am, maybe I'm not. I have little doubt I am not. The plain fact is I don't enjoy working here any more.'

'We don't get paid our vast salaries to enjoy ourselves, Francis. If it was wonderful fun they wouldn't pay us so much to do it. We'd pay for the privilege.'

'Don't teach your grandmother how to suck eggs, Chris. I've been in this business too long. I am perfectly acquainted with the inescapable fact that it is far from milk and honey. Yet it should not be necessary to force myself to get up each morning, to drag myself here by the scruff of my own collar, against my will, knowing I will be treated like an old busybody, a nonentity, an irrelevance.'

'Bullshit! Everyone here has the highest respect for your creative judgment.'

'Everyone? Ask your young darlings Nathan and O'Reilly whether or not they respect my creative judgment. And when you were first presented with their Splashasoap campaign you were more influenced by Dave Horrell's opinion than mine. So was Flora. Neither of you were the least bit interested in my comments. The Creative Director's comments. You were convinced by the Media Director. Horrell! He couldn't tell a Pierra della Francesca from a Pierre Renoir toilet water!'

'We're talking about advertising, Francis. Not fine art.'

'I thought we were talking about creative judgment. My creative judgment.'

'Advertising's about communicating with the man in the street. And Dave Horrell is, well, sometimes, a pretty typical example of the man in the street. He's not as sophisticated as you and me.'

'So make him Creative Director. The job's vacant.'

Looking at Francis Kemp-Lewis across his desk, Chris noticed how much smaller he looked than he really was, shrunk by his own insecurity. Nervously jabbing his unlit pipe in and out of his mouth, white flecks of dry saliva collecting at the edges of his lips, his normally proud bow tie limp and haggard, the Vicar was having a rough time of it. Egos! Nobody outside of advertising would ever dream how much of an agency Chief Executive's time was spent soothing and smoothing subordinates' frayed egos. Not that he was making a terribly good job of it on this occasion, Chris admitted to himself. Much of what the Vicar was saying was too true to contradict convincingly; in the matter of bruised egos it almost always was.

'You've not told me if you've got another job.'

'Is it any of your business?'

'Not if you think otherwise.'

'Look. I've been hanging on here, hating every single day of it, every minute of every hour, because I've been waiting to be fired. Because that's in my interest. Tax-free compensation for loss of office. A sizeable sum after seventeen years. Now I'm willing to go quietly. Without causing trouble, without grumbling to clients, not to Marmaduke or anyone. If you pay me off.'

'I don't want to pay you off. It's you talking of quitting. Why should Pendletons pay you off?'

'Because otherwise I'll make things nasty.'

'You are. Already.'

'Pay me off, and I won't.'

'Francis, see sense, for God's sake,' Chris said, wishing immediately that he had not invoked the Almighty's name because it might irritate the Vicar. 'If you've no job to go to there's no point in leaving. If you are determined to go – against my wishes – then take your time, look around, wait till you've found a good job. Don't quit in pique, because of something Dave Horrell said when he was drunk. It's stupid.'

'Don't you think I've been looking? At my age it's not easy. And I've given the best years of my life to Pendletons. Which has done nothing to enhance my creative reputation, I can assure you. I want the money.'

'What money? You know I can't afford to pay you off. We're struggling to make our profit target as it is. You know that. It's how this all started. What do you want me to do? Fire another nineteen non-existent cleaners?'

Francis did not answer at once. Instead he stared at Chris, sitting in his self-important Hepplewhite chair, trying to look firm and authoritative and powerful, but in reality a puppet on New York's strings, still wearing red braces to impress the Americans with his English dignity, but looking smaller than he really was, shrunken by the pressures and nastiness of the job. 'You know it's all round the agency already?'

'What is?'

'That you intend firing the cleaners. To save money. The staff think it's because we're going to lose Splashasoap to ACM – they don't think we stand a chance – and the Americans have ordered you to make cutbacks. That's the rumour.'

'Christ!' Chris cried, once again regretting his blasphemy, 'how do they know? Who told them? It's not even been finally decided!'

'Not I. It's not for me to say. But remember that some of those present at our discussion went on to the pub afterwards. And they were drunk when they got there. And so were lots of the staff.'

'Oh my . . . Hell.' This time Chris restrained himself. 'How can anybody run an organisation like this? It's impossible.'

'Rumours spread like wildfire in all organisations, Chris. There's nothing special about this one.'

Chris Beaumont stood up and paced slowly around the room, staring at the floor, his feet dragging themselves behind each other across the plush carpet. Nobody could be trusted, he thought, nobody. It was discouraging, disillusioning, disgusting.

'Are you going to pay me off?'

'You know I can't. I won't. How could I explain it to New York? If you quit, you quit.'

Francis thought for a moment before speaking again. 'You know Marmaduke are going to give us another brand? Wodgits, probably. They told me last week when I dined with them. In confidence. That's why I've said nothing. It's worth four million. But I could stop them. If I tried.'

Chris was stunned. An additional £4 million from Marmaduke would compensate for Pierre Renoir and leave sufficient over to make up the profit shortfall Boyne was demanding. So long as Pendletons held on to Larsons – and he was confident they could – everything would be all right, it would be unnecessary to fire anyone.

'Why didn't you mention this on Thursday evening? It changes everything.'

'And have Dave Horrell go blurting it round the pub? I was

told in strictest confidence. Marmaduke haven't even told PPL they will be losing Wodgits yet.'

'When will they?' Timing, Chris had rapidly realised, was of the essence.

'This week, they said. But you know Marmaduke. It could take them months. They're waiting for the decision to be rubber-stamped by HQ in Tulsa.'

'So when will they tell us? Officially?'

'How should I know? Next week I should think. If all goes well.'

'Before or after the Larsons pitch, do you think?'

'I've no idea. When they get round to it, I expect.' The Vicar hesitated. 'Unless I tell them I'm leaving beforehand. That would give them pause, I assume.'

That was probably, Chris thought, the first time in his life that Francis Kemp-Lewis had tried to blackmail anyone, and he patently did not enjoy doing it one bit. Vicars, he thought, are not designed to be in advertising.

'Listen, Francis,' he said, 'if you're willing to trust me I'll make sure you get the money you want. First tell me honestly: have you a new job lined up?'

'Not . . . no.'

'I take it you're close to one?'

'I think so. They've not decided yet.'

'How soon will it be before you know?'

'Weeks at least. If I get it at all. It's a charity job. They take ages. Endless committees. You know the form. That's why I need the money.'

'OK I'll make this agreement with you. But neither of us must ever mention it to a soul. Never.'

The Vicar disliked the notion of a conspiracy, but nonetheless nodded his assent.

'You withdraw your resignation,' Chris spoke quickly, 'until after the Larsons pitch and, more importantly, until after we've gained Wodgits. Then I tell Bob Boyne that with the extra billings at last we can afford a new Creative Director. Then I'll fire you and pay you off generously. Is that a deal?'

'So . . . ' The Vicar drew hard, almost desperately, on his pipe.

'So . . . you have wanted to fire me all the time, Chris. Exactly as I said.'

Chris was aghast at his mistake. 'Rubbish! It was just a turn of phrase, a slip of the tongue. Don't take it so personally, Francis!'

'How else can I take it? I bring in more business from Marmaduke, so *at last* you can afford to fire me and get a new Creative Director!'

'It's what you wanted, Francis. It was your suggestion, not mine.'

Francis Kemp-Lewis stood up and walked to the door, stuffing his pipe in his baggy jacket pocket, his mind absorbed with his own thoughts. 'I hate this place,' he said, turning to Chris, 'hate it, hate it!'

'Well, will you agree to the deal? It's in your interests, Francis. It really is. You can trust me.'

'Trust you? Yes, I'll agree to it. And I'll stick by it.'

Trying hard not to show how relieved he was, Chris leapt across to him. 'Shall we shake on it?'

'I don't want to shake hands with you, Christopher. Let us simply stick to our agreement. That is all that is necessary.'

'You've got my word. I've never broken my word, Francis.'

'I'm sure you haven't Christopher, I'm sure you haven't.'

'It's most kind of you to agree to this meeting at such short notice. Most kind. I won't keep you long.'

'No trouble, Mr Dalrymple. No trouble at all.'

'I simply felt that – after that unfortunate story in *Campaign* last Thursday – that perhaps I had been somewhat remiss in not visiting you earlier. I know Mr Digby has been in, and he has recommended you most highly. I believe he worked with one of you? At an earlier stage of his career?'

Peter Dalrymple was one of those people who (though enjoying perfect eyesight) barely noticed his surroundings. So he was unable to pinpoint precisely the peculiarities of Gilbernetti, Orr and Burton's décor. Nonetheless, as he had waited for a moment in reception and now sat across the table from the three of them in their variegated boardroom, he sensed that GOB lacked the style, the dash, the panache of ACM. The obsessions that agency people had with décor were not wholly misguided.

Following his reassuring interrogation of Des Digby he had concluded that it would be neither fair nor just – nor in Larsons' best interests – to discard Gilbernetti, Orr and Burton too precipitately. So he had informed Des Digby that he wished to visit them, alone, as quickly as possible.

This had caused Des Digby to spend a tormented weekend. He could not decide whether or not to telephone Hal and warn him of the real purpose of Dalrymple's visit. His initial inclination was to do so. Indeed he had asked his secretary to put him through to GOB on Friday afternoon – then instantly cancelled the call. The more he considered the matter the more complicated it became.

He could not believe that Dalrymple would admit he had received (and, more importantly, been influenced by) the anonymous letter. How could he even mention it, to people he did not know, had never met before? Nor, without mentioning the letter, could he possibly ask direct questions about the incriminating evening: 'Excuse me, Mr Burton, but did you buy our Mr Digby a whore? I mean, Mr Burton, in order to get on the Splashasoap short list did you bankroll my marketing manager the price of a fuck with the luscious Vera?' It was unthinkable. Dalrymple would never raise the issue openly.

On the other hand, he would not be visiting GOB to discuss the ever-escalating cost of peak-time spots in *Coronation Street*, or the comparative statistical reliability of random and quota sampling. He was going there to verify the truth of Des's denial. Des was sure Dalrymple was already eighty per cent convinced, but wanted to be one hundred per cent – or at least ninety nine per cent – convinced before letting the matter drop. So he would raise it obliquely, rather than outright. Quite how, Des could not imagine. Should he or should he not warn Hal in advance? The danger was that Hal – whose skills as a liar Des had good reason, he felt, not to rate highly – would become so nervous he would betray himself unwittingly. Whereas if he thought Dalrymple simply wanted to meet the agency, the event would doubtless pass off smoothly, without anyone being any the wiser.

'We worked at Beechams together. When we were still in knee-pants!' Hal laughed edgily, and Peter Dalrymple smiled politely. 'Des came in as a trainee when I was a product manager. He was a bright lad. One of the brightest. But then I need hardly tell you that, Mr Dalrymple.'

Conversation ceased while coffee was served, and James Orr noticed, to his fury, that Dalrymple's cup was slightly chipped. Should he offer to change it? Better to let sleeping dogs lie. Dalrymple didn't seem like the kind of chap who would worry about a chipped cup. Probably hadn't even noticed it. But how incredibly stupid the secretaries were! They knew, everybody in the agency knew, Peter Dalrymple was an important prospective client. He would speak to them afterwards.

'Perhaps you'd kindly tell me a little about the agency, and then show me your television reel,' Peter Dalrymple said, turning the chip away from his lips, 'and then I can ask a few questions if I may. I don't want to take up too much of your time.'

With as much eloquence and enthusiasm as he could muster James Orr launched into his well-worn sales patter. They had started the agency five years ago believing they had a unique combination of talents to offer. Irving Gilbernetti brought American advertising know-how and drive to UK advertising: 'As everyone knows, Mr Dalrymple, America is the home of advertising, and though we British like to pride ourselves on our creativity, the unpalatable fact is, as research has proved time and again, American advertising is at least four times more sales effective than British advertising.' (One day, Hal Burton often thought, somebody is going to challenge James to produce that mythical research; but nobody ever did.)

In Hal Burton, James meanwhile continued, the agency had one of the country's leading marketing men, with experience on both client and agency sides of the fence, having worked in senior positions at Beechams, Allied Breweries and Norwich Union before switching over to become research and planning director at Young and Rubicam, and then joining forces with Irving and himself. As for himself (he said modestly) he was a plain and simple businessman, who had trained as an accountant, having started at Peat Marwick before moving into cost accountancy with British Leyland ('an invaluable apprenticeship in learning how not to do things, I'm afraid') and then working for several multinational advertising agencies before catching the irresistible entrepreneurial bug to be one's own boss and run one's own show.

'We believed our blend of real American creativity, marketing experience and financial acumen would provide clients with something special. The best of America, the best of British united in one team and one team only: Gilbernetti, Orr and Burton. And our record so far, Mr Dalrymple, shows we weren't wrong. Our impressive client list, our growth and our success' – here even James faltered perceptibly – 'proved' – here James grinned confidently to recapture the lost point – 'proves we must have been doing something right. Very right indeed. Now, if we may, we'd like to show you our reel.'

Throughout James's monologue – which each of them had heard several dozen times before – Irving Gilbernetti and Hal Burton had attempted to look bright-eyed and interested. With each successive rendition over the years, both of them found it more and more unconvincing and embarrassing. However, when they had jointly faced James Orr with their criticisms about six months previously (and only after weeks of prior clandestine discussion between the two of them), he had challenged them to think of something better. They had so far failed. So their sole achievement had been the undermining of James's confidence, and thereafter he sounded less convincing than ever. Not that this had proved a significant handicap in their new business endeavours, as James had only been required to deliver his agency sales pitch three times in the preceding six months: once to Des Digby, once to a putative advertiser who had patented a new method of conserving Indonesian sauces, but had not as yet managed to amass the wherewithal to advertise his spicy invention, and once to a group of Nigerian students.

Peter Dalrymple then watched their show-reel of TV commercials, with desultory attention. Some clients – clients who read *Campaign* assiduously each week and take an urgent interest in advertising and advertising agency gossip – love to watch agencies' TV reels. Peter was not one of them. Being far more interested in content than in execution, in the message than in the style, he was not especially interested in the name of the lighting-cameraman, or which laboratory produced the optical effects. He wanted to be told only the marketing objectives and the sales results, and these, he knew from experience, no agency would truthfully tell him. As a result he generally found the viewing of agencies' TV reels, with their hand-picked selections of the agency's fifteen or twenty 'best' commercials, an unenlightening experience. He was suspicious of commercials which were too clever, or witty, or pretty, and bored by those which weren't.

'Very impressive,' he said as the reel ended, and Irving Gilbernetti thanked him warmly for his appreciation. 'And now perhaps I might take up just five more minutes of your precious time? First – I do hope these questions don't sound too aggressive – I wondered why you thought Mr Digby had put you on our short list. I mean, what have you to offer Larsons that's different from any other agency?'

'Well,' James Orr replied, 'in the first place Hal Burton obviously has tremendous knowledge of toiletry marketing. From his days in Beecham. And then, as I mentioned before, Irving's American approach to creativity has been proved successful in the UK market.'

'And I worked with P and G too, way back. In the States, I mean. There's not much about toiletries them Cincinatti giants don't know. So that's pretty good experience too.'

'Anything else, Mr Burton?'

'My partners have said it all, I think.'

'Yes indeed. Very impressive. Now, on a different matter, I wondered what your general views of entertaining clients are.'

'I . . . I don't quite follow, Mr Dalrymple,' James replied. It was not a question he had ever previously encountered during such a presentation.

'Well, I wondered what your agency's general approach was. Do you have any rules or guidelines for your staff for instance?'

'We sure do!' Irving responded cheerfully. 'We're mean as hell! We tell our guys we want clients to appoint us for the work, not for the booze. That's the old-fashioned way, Mr Dalrymple. We don't believe in it here at GOB. I'm sorry, Mr Dalrymple, but if entertaining's what you're after you'll have to look elsewhere.'

'I'm sure that's not what Mr Dalrymple meant,' James interrupted his partner tetchily.

'Certainly not. But that was a very full and helpful answer. At Larsons we like to have these things out on the table, and may I say we agree with your views wholeheartedly, Mr Gilbernetti. Wholeheartedly.'

Peter Dalrymple was irritable that he was failing to get through to Hal Burton. All his questions were being intercepted by the other two, which was not what he had intended. He had not expected Hal Burton to be so reticent and retiring a character. Chubby and friendly, he certainly didn't look like a whoremonger. 'I'm also rather concerned, Mr Burton,' he said, 'though it may sound silly to you, about your friendship with Mr Digby. Such things can cause difficulties. And rumours and so on. They're so easily misunderstood.'

'Well . . . we're not exactly close friends, Mr Dalrymple.'

'Are you not? I understood otherwise from Mr Digby.'

'Not really. We've hardly met since we worked at Beechams together.'

'Really? I must have misunderstood. When did you last meet, for example?'

'When Des, Mr Digby, visited the agency to see our presentation. Before putting us on your short list.'

'And did you, for example, get involved in any entertaining on that occasion?'

'Well, yes . . . we went out to dinner at a cheap Italian trattoria I know. Nothing very grand, I can tell you.'

'That's all?'

'What do you mean, that's all?' Hal smiled self-consciously, and forced a strained grin.

'That's all you did?'

'Yes. Apart from a couple of drinks beforehand.' Hal could feel beads of sweat trickling down his armpits, and breaking out like raindrops on his forehead. He longed to wipe them away but feared that would draw too much attention to them.

His bowels were turning to water; at any moment he might be compelled to make an incriminating dash to the lavatory. Clenching his fists tightly beneath the table, he prayed that Dalrymple could not perceive the strain he felt, and forced another counterfeit grin. Thank God Des had phoned and warned him. But had he in turn been right not to apprise James and Irving of the real purpose of Dalrymple's visit? 'Is there something particular on your mind, Mr Dalrymple?'

'No. Nothing at all. We're an old-fashioned company, and I merely wanted to get your idea of what you thought was an acceptable level of client entertainment. So we have no problems in future, you see. We are rather fuddy-duddy I suppose. But that's our way.'

'You've got standards, Mr Dalrymple,' Irving said softly, 'and we respect that.'

'Excellent. Excellent. We obviously see eye to eye. I don't want to labour the point, but it's better to be safe than sorry. Now I must be going. I look forward to seeing your Splashasoap presentation. I look forward to it very much indeed.'

'I know you can defend the figure, Bob, and I know you've good arguments but $540 million is still out of the question... Yes, I know you've already come down $60 million, but you're losing business from your London office at a rate of knots... I know you're planning to put it right but from our side $380 million is the maximum Pendletons is worth. Not a penny more... OK, then, let's forget it. Maybe another time, Bob. It's been good talking to you.'

Stan Isaacs put the phone down and wondered whether Bob Boyne was still bluffing or whether that, finally, was that.

VIII
Ramifications

'Can I speak to Trevor?' Susan cooed into the phone.

'Can I ask who's calling?' replied a strong-willed voice.

'Just say . . . ' Susan lowered her voice to its sexiest, 'just say it's personal.'

'Trevor, er, Mr Kidd will want to know who's calling.'

This one was not going to be a pushover. In order to bypass obstructing secretaries, Susan's instructions were to sound as much like a mistress as she knew how. It was one of Isaacs and Isaacs' most creative new business ploys. 'Just tell Trevor it's . . . rather urgent.' If her voice dropped any lower, she thought, she'd be talking through her toenails.

'May I ask what it's about?'

'Trev'll know.'

A series of clicks at the other end indicated that the obstructive secretary had succumbed to Susan's seduction.

'Hallo,' Trevor Kidd's nasal voice came on the line, 'can I help you?'

Susan's voice snapped from sultry to crisp. 'Good morning, Mr Kidd. I have Mr Charles Kelly of Isaacs and Isaacs for you.'

'Isaacs and Isaacs?' Trevor asked into the void, as Susan transferred the call to her boss.

'Mr Kidd? This is Charles Kelly of Isaacs and Isaacs.'

'Mr Kelly? To what do I owe the pleasure?'

'Well, Mr Kidd' Kelly slipped into his sales pitch with far more certainty and confidence than James Orr; but then he had far more to be certain and confident about. He smiled into the telephone (on the telephone a smiling voice sounds friendlier – the telephone salesman's eleven key rules of power-packed persuasion, rule one), 'here at Isaacs and Isaacs,' (mention Isaacs and Isaacs' name quickly because nobody rings off on a highly successful company, rule two) 'we like to keep track of major and important advertisers like Crispins Squashes' (flattery will get you everywhere, rule three), 'and we have recently carried out some market research into squash advertising, and particularly Crispins' advertising, which we are certain will be of interest to you,' (titillate the prospect, rule four). 'I wonder if you would have the time to visit us in the near future for a brief presentation of the research findings?' (offer the customer a benefit quickly, rule five).

Silence emanated from the Crispins end of the line; a much longer silence than Charles Kelly was accustomed to. Surely he had not said anything wrongly? Might he have been cut off in mid-patter? 'Mr Kidd? Are you there?'

'Still here, Mr Kelly, have no fear. I am contemplating your proposition. Can you tell me a little more about this, er, research you have carried out for us?'

'I'd sooner not go into it further at this stage, Mr Kidd, if you don't mind. It's only a pilot study of course, but the results are quite detailed,' (once they are nibbling at the bait don't let them off the hook, rule six). 'Have you got your diary handy? How about next Tuesday or Wednesday?' (be specific and try to close the sale rapidly, rule seven).

'It's very kind of you to offer, Mr Kelly, very kind of you indeed, if I may say so. May I also take this opportunity to say I have for many years, if not longer, held your agency in the highest esteem. Isaacs and Isaacs is an agency whose reputation goes before it, in my humble opinion. But we're satisfied customers with our present agency, Gilbernetti, Orr and Burton, though, so it would not be the right thing to make a visit to your own shop at this moment in time.'

'I do understand, Mr Kidd, entirely. And there's nothing we at Isaacs and Isaacs respect more than a faithful client! We certainly won't be trying to get your advertising account, I can assure you! We dislike that kind of salesmanship as much as I'm sure you do. This is simply a presentation of market research data which may be of use to Crispins. Without any commitment at all,' (don't ask for too much commitment too soon, rule eight).

There was another pause. Trevor Kidd had not learned a great deal during his long years as a Brand Manager, but he had learned how not to be hustled. 'I am not unappreciative of your comments, Mr Kelly, not at all. But rumours do get about you know. My goodness they do, though. And Isaacs and Isaacs are not exactly strangers to the pages of *Campaign*, if you get my meaning.'

'Your visit to us would be in the strictest confidence, Mr Kidd. I can promise you. There would be no publicity whatsoever, you have my word,' (overcome objections with complete sincerity, rule nine).

'Well I'm sure I can trust *you*, Mr Kelly, if you give me your word. Even though we've never met. But walls have ears you know!'

It was an objection Charles Kelly found difficult to overcome. Perhaps he should point out to the old fool that Isaacs and Isaacs had special walls, which were stone deaf? 'So what day should we make it, Mr Kidd? I could make Friday, if Tuesday or Wednesday are not convenient.'

'Thank you, Mr Kelly, but I really don't believe in going the rounds of agencies. At Crispins we do like to be, as you put it, faithful. And we're happy enough with Gilbernetti, Orr and Burton. We've only been with them for four years. Or maybe four and a half. And they're a very fine agency, you know.'

'Indeed they are, Mr Kidd, no doubt about it,' (never disagree with the prospect, rule ten) 'but, for example, oughtn't you to keep your options open? I mean, what if something happened to them?'

'What kind of thing do you have in mind?'

'Well . . . anything really,' (not specific enough, remember rule six!).

'They're not being bought up by Isaacs and Isaacs are they?'

'Hell, no!'

'Because in my opinion you blighters would like to gobble up every good agency in the country. If you don't mind me saying so.'

'Well, Mr Kidd! I don't know about that, Mr Kidd!' (when all else fails, keep repeating the customer's name: a man's name is the sweetest sound in the world to him, rule eleven).

'Don't think I'm not flattered by the interest the mighty

Isaacs and Isaacs have taken in Crispins Squashes, Mr Kelly. I'm most appreciative indeed. Not at this moment in time, though thank you.' Who did the young scallywag think he was fooling? Trevor Kidd smiled to himself as he put down the receiver. Pilot research indeed! Probably one group discussion in Croydon. As if a leading company like Crispins needed Isaacs and Isaacs to do its market research for it. As if we don't do our own research, and plenty of it. Those Isaacs and Isaacs boys think they can rule the world. Well, he'd told them where to get off. He would have to tell Irving and Hal about it next time he saw them. It would be a good laugh.

It is little fun being a vulture, Charles Kelly groaned as he put down the receiver, when the carcase is so unyielding. Thank heaven he had wasted no money on commissioning the pilot research, prior to Kidd agreeing to make a visit. But Ralph would not be pleased, not be pleased at all.

    To: Chris Beaumont
    From: Bob Boyne

1. Excellent news re Wodgits. Understand confidentianess. Will tell nobody but Eddie, Larry and Chuck. Pass enthusiastic congratulations to ill concerned.
2. Ensure gain is not frittered away in extra costs. All new income should flow straight to bottom line. Marmaduke is a fine, profitable account. Let's keep it that way.
3. Accept yo argument. Wodgits gain cancels need for immediate staff cuts per previous telexes, unless cuts will streamline UK operation anyway which in my view has grown too fat. Your comments please.
4. All above dependent on holding Larsons. Hope your optimism is justified but essential you have contingency plans as Pierre Renoir on way out due to lousy servicing worldwide. Minus Pierre Renoir minus Larsons plus Wodgits equals zilch. Maybe less than zilch. Get Ron Dark to check urgently and confirm by telex.
5. If you luse Larsons imperative you make cutbacks next day or sooner as this is good management, also saves money. No point in holding staff once account gone. Could Flora Thompson be saving?

She's expensive. What else does she work on? Also other Larsons/Pierre Renoir pople. They won't be needed on Wodgits. Repeat imperative cutbacks follow Larsons loss without delay. New worldwide company policy, endorsed by Eddie.

6   What progress cutting entertainment expenses? Still await list of big sponders.

7   Re Wodgits, let me have names of persons responsible for winning business, secretaries inclusive, and I'll get Eddie's PA to send Eddie's personal thank yous when appropriate. Say wehn.

Will phone you at weekend when I get home from Santiago to discuss Larsons loss contingency flan. With my very best wishes and warmest regards.

Bob.

As it turned out, Harry Adams' anonymous letter suited each of Gilbernetti Orr and Burton quite well. In the resulting hiatus the possibility of employing Greg Hamilton to research Irving Gilbernetti's campaign was forgotten; this made Irving a most happy fellow. The money saved made James Orr a happy fellow too. Peter Dalrymple having visited the agency and evidently not found it too repellent, James pointed out that wasting money on decorators was now pointless, a point his colleagues saw no reason to dispute. For his part Hal Burton, as chief defendant in the dramatic case of Dalrymple v. GOB, had successfully bluffed his way out of trouble, and the agency back on to the Larsons' short list, an achievement for which he not unnaturally assumed his partners should be eternally grateful. Above all, the lifting of the tension under which the three of them had been living for the previous seventy-two hours produced the kind of manic elation which advertising agency people normally associate only with the winning of major new clients: a heady, devil-may-care combination of relaxation, financial gain and competitive victory – doubtless similar to the emotions of victorious racing drivers at the end of a gruelling Grand Prix, and not dissimilarly bathed in booze. But Gilbernetti, Orr and Burton had as yet won nothing. They had still to beat Pendletons, the incumbent agency, and ACM, the hottest shop in town, to stay in business.

It was an unpleasant reality they kept forcing themselves to remember.

Still, they were in an optimistic and cheerful mood when they foregathered in their boardroom on the afternoon of Peter Dalrymple's visit to hear Irving Gilbernetti present his much heralded and much postponed creative solution to the Splashasoap problem. Those present, in addition to the triumvirate, were Alec Doughty, one of GOB's two elderly account executives and an excellent golfer, and Steve 'Meany' Hudson, their Media Manager whom they boasted was the meanest media buyer in town, but who was palpably a sweetie and soft as a bankrupt publication's rate-card. Irving had insisted that 'Meany' and Alec should be present – 'we gotta have objective outsiders' views on this one' – and both were flattered. Alec was especially gratified because he had been selected in preference to Bill Shelford, GOB's other Account Director (Alec and Bill always described themselves, incorrectly, as directors), despite the fact that Bill was more experienced (equals older) and an even better golfer. In fact Hal Burton, who had selected Alec rather than Bill for the project, knew that while both of them could slaughter Des Digby on the golf course neither of them was any kind of match for him in any other respect. He had chosen Alec, without much enthusiasm, because he looked six or seven years the younger. Small, unsuccessful agencies don't have the pick of the crop.

'Now,' said Irving, who had had more than sufficient opportunity to rehearse his opening remarks during the previous days, 'all you guys know I'm no way great at research. I'm only the Creative Director and to me tables of figures are pains in the arse. But a few nights back, as I happen to be some kinda masochist for this agency, I found myself reading the Larsons' documents they sent us, and suddenly it came clear. You don't need a masters in statistics. Even a simple creative guy can see the trouble. Splashasoap costs too much! That's it. The whole schmeer. As it says here on page thirty-seven: "The deterrent factor to purchasing, among those non-users who accepted the product benefits, was its expense. Splashasoap is seen by this sizeable sector as being in the luxury, indulgent mode, and they are therefore resistant to using it on an everyday basis. They see it for bathroom use and not kitchens, as a small gift and not self-purchase. This is not a price/income correlation, similar negative responses being identified among housewives of all social classes. The predominant mode among this group of housewives is that they like the *idea* of liquid soaps but cannot justify to themselves the *cost*." Get it?'

'Get it? Of course we get it. It's in the brief,' James responded tetchily.

While Irving had lunched alone at his desk, James and Hal had gone out together – an uncommon gesture of friendship these days – and quaffed a celebratory bottle of Lanson Black Label, with a couple of smoked salmon sandwiches, in Sparklers Champagne Bar. Over lunch each had revealed to the other his private anxieties concerning Irving's ability to handle this vital new business pitch. They even agreed, as the bottle emptied, that they would insist on Irving hiring a freelance creative team ('and fuck the cost,' James asserted expansively) to work on the pitch if Irving's own ideas were not up to scratch. As they repeatedly told each other, this was the one they could not afford to lose. They could not risk the agency going bust by continuing to pander to Irving's sensibilities. They had done so too long. Bucked by their newly-found bravura they returned to the agency in an even more buoyant frame of mind than they had left it, ready to give Irving a hard time ('if need be, but we mustn't pre-judge').

'Right. It's in the brief. So it came from Larsons. So they ain't gonna quarrel with it? Right?'

'We all know Splashasoap's got a price problem. So what's new?'

'Listen, will you! Being as how neither of you guys has written me a creative strategy I've written it myself.' Irving then held up a white board on which he had neatly lettered, in black magic marker:

Splashasoap

Creative Strategy

> To persuade housewives, who like the idea of liquid soaps but feel guilty they're a waste of cash, that Splashasoap's the 'in' thing to be using!

'I don't get it,' James Orr responded unhelpfully.

155

'It's simple!' Irving pressed on unabashed. 'We want to justify Splashasoap's price, we make it a classy product. The product every housewife uses to be one jump ahead. We make using Splashasoap the smart thing to do.'

At this point Alec Doughty felt it necessary to make a contribution, and dredged a famous campaign of long ago from his memory. 'You mean like "Top People Take *The Times*", Irving?'

'Yeah ... well, not exactly. We can't equate Splashasoap with *The Times* exactly,' Irving chuckled at the thought, 'but the strategy's pretty much the same.'

'It's not believable,' Hal Burton stated.

'Who says? It depends how it's done, you schmuck.' Irving was not easily to be deflected from the ideas which had been gestating in his mind and on his drawing board for almost a week. 'Can't you be anything but negative? That's the trouble with this damn agency. You and James are real great at saying no, but you ain't got the balls to say yes ever.'

Hal and James looked at each other, and then at Alec and Meany. Bad though relations between the three partners had become, they avoided quarrelling in front of the staff. (Or rather they imagined they did. In fact the staff frequently heard their bosses bickering, and indeed over-dramatised – rather than minimised – the hostilities.) By starting to squabble in the presence of Alec and Meany, James and Hal each thought to himself, Irving was deviously hoping to squash any opposition. That, they both concluded, had been why he insisted on Alec and Meany being there. Well, they decided, we'll soon see about that. Irving, in contrast, saw the debate as the usual thrust and parry between creative and uncreative people, and felt himself to be just getting into his stride.

'It's unbelievable however you do it,' Hal insisted. 'It's impossible to make Splashasoap a classy product. Look at the pack. It's downmarket, unexciting, housewifey and plain dull. It's about as fashionable as lisle stockings!'

'Right! You're getting it. First we gotta re-do the pack. I had a few shots at it.' Irving displayed a card on which were six new Splashasoap pack designs. While none of them was going to win a Designers and Art Directors' Award for astonishing originality, all were notably more stylish, more expensive-looking than the existing pack which Irving had placed next to them.

'Very nice,' said Alec Doughty dutifully.

'Yes, I like those,' agreed Meany, 'especially the red and green one. And the purple one. And the beige one too.'

Hal and James, to their chagrin, were not unimpressed.

'The beige one's got no shelf-impact,' Hal said, putting Meany in his place, 'you'd never see it in Tescos. But the red and green one's not bad. In fact . . . it's pretty good.'

'There you go,' Irving was gleeful at having carried his audience so far; 'like I say, it's how you do it that counts. So we get the pack neat. Not *Vogue*, not *Harpers*, but a little more *Cosmo*. So before we get to the ads, let's look at some promotions. Until now, Larsons have treated Splashasoap like a typical grocery line. Five pence off, ten pence off your next purchase, two-packs banded together and all that crap. If we're gonna make Splashasoap the smartest thing since designer labels, all that's disastersville. You don't buy Brooks Brothers' suits with money-off vouchers!'

'If Splashasoap isn't *The Times*, it's hardly a Brooks Brothers' suit either,' interrupted James Orr, who found Irving's loquacity terribly tiresome.

'Maybe so. But it mustn't be a schlock bargain-basement brand either. Not at eighty-nine pence a pack. So we tell Larsons in future they do only class promotions, image promotions, this kinda stuff.' Irving picked up another three white boards and rapidly flipped through them. Each displayed a simple design for a display showcard: 'Ten guineas off your next Hermes scarf, with Splashasoap'; 'Win a holiday at St James's Club, Antigua, with Splashasoap'; 'Visit the Paris collections, with Splashasoap'.

'Neat uh? High rollin' stuff. Nothing but the best for Splashasoap.'

'Hardly likely to go down big with C2 housewives in Wigan,' Hal Burton commented.

'So what's it matter? We only get a handful of entries or redemptions, who cares? This is an image-job I keep telling you. We gotta upgrade Splashasoap's image. Right now it's the pits.'

'Isn't guineas rather old fashioned?' asked Meany. 'I thought we were trying to modernise Splashasoap.'

'That's what I was going to say,' echoed Alec, irritable that his thunder had been stolen.

'That's exactly it,' snapped Irving, 'it's not old fashioned, it's yesterday. And today yesterday is tomorrow.'

'I think it's good,' James judicially opined, not having previously uttered. 'I think you're on to something. I've never seen high-class promotions like that in supermarkets.'

'I'm not disagreeing,' Hal concurred, 'not at all. But we'll have to make clear to Larsons we realise soft promotions like these don't bring huge extra sales.'

'Sure, sure we will,' Irving brushed aside the trivial issue. 'So now let's get to the ads.'

'Hang on a sec,' – it was Alec Doughty again – 'what about proof of purchase?'

'Proof of purchase?' Irving was nonplussed.

'Promotions like these always require customers to prove they've purchased. How can they prove they've bought Splashasoap? They can't send in a whole pack.'

Irving pondered this logistical snag. A typical Alec Doughty point, he thought. 'We'll hang a leaflet round the pack's necks. I'll do a little mock-up. Now can I get on with the ads already?'

About three-quarters of an hour later the meeting was ready to disperse. Hal and James were exuberant. They could hardly believe what they'd seen, but Irving had done it, he'd really done it. He still had it in him after all. The campaign was original, exciting, creative and logical. It could not fail to persuade every housewife in the country that bar soaps were behind the times and Splashasoap was the stylish way to wash in the 1980s. There had only been one hiccup during Irving's presentation, when Meany had pointed out that Irving had written forty-second commercials, but on the Splashasoap budget only thirty-second spots, at the longest, could be afforded.

Irving would have no truck with such pedantry. 'It's a new

business pitch, I'm telling you. We win the business, we worry about the spots. At new business pitches it's ideas that count. Creativity. Clients don't want to know about spot lengths. Spot lengths are *boring*.'

Hal and James backed their Creative Director and Meany was squashed. Irving was given a £2,500 budget to pre-record the commercial sound-tracks, for extra impact, and to get the television commercial storyboards and press ads finished up professionally (a budget which, in the event, he would overspend by a hundred per cent). Meany was detailed to produce media-buying recommendations which would support Irving's campaign. Hal Burton's job was to write a document and summarise it on slides, which would use Larsons' own brief and research to prove unequivocally that Irving's approach was the correct one – the only correct one, and nothing but the correct one. Alec Doughty was instructed to orchestrate and synthesise everyone's efforts. And James Orr returned home that evening, for the first time in many, many months, feeling like the boss of a dynamic, well-organised, and successful advertising agency.

Harry Adams was not enjoying his chat with Paul O'Reilly. If Paul were to be believed, Pendletons was in complete chaos. There was no leadership, no management, no control. People were being hired and fired randomly, as if their names had been flung into a hat and plucked out by blindfold butchers. Paul had heard that – only a few months after being hired – he and Tom Nathan were now to be chopped; that the Vicar was to be chopped; that Flora Thompson was to be chopped; that there were people in every department on the hit list. Even the old cleaning ladies were to be chopped, and everyone was going to have to clean their own offices in future; everyone said Chris Beaumont was going too, and Ron Dark would be taking over as a caretaker Chairman until they found a Yank who would run things the way New York wanted them run.

And it was all, Paul said everybody said, because they had already lost Splashasoap to ACM. The forthcoming presentations were mere charades. Everyone knew that Pendletons couldn't beat ACM; and everyone included Larsons. Look at the shortlist: Pendletons, GOB and ACM. It had to be a set-up. Des Digby wanted ACM, so he had made up a duff short list to legitimise his decision. And Pendletons now knew it. That was why they were firing so many people.

The two questions to which Paul urgently needed answers were: first, was it all true? Second, would Harry object if he and Tom Nathan accepted the job at ACM which had now formally been offered them? – since otherwise he was likely to be unemployed in a week or so, when the Pendletons' guillotine started falling. ('Not that me and Tom can't find a job. But there's not so many agencies as we want to work at. And I'm finding it difficult explaining to Tom why we shouldn't take the ACM offer, you see.')

None of which Harry found easy to answer. Things at the agency had moved on apace in the previous twenty-four hours. First, and predictably, Bill McAndrew had sided with Mike in the anonymous letter dispute. Bill too thought Harry's behaviour shoddy and reprehensible; but hailing from Glasgow's roughest neighbourhood he was not as shocked as all that. He wanted to dissociate himself from Harry's action; he would never behave similarly himself; but many people did, in business and in life. So he was unsure about it being sufficient reason to withdraw from the Splashasoap race. Particularly not now they had come so far, and done so much work on rejuvenating Splashasoap to give it a new, young, lively image.

Second, and utterly unpredictably, as the dispute was reaching its inconclusive end, the Marketing Director of Unigamble had telephoned and asked – off the record, strictly confidentially and out of the blue – whether ACM would be interested in handling one of their toilet soap brands. He was unwilling to specify which, at this stage, but said it was not one of their biggest. 'Billings of less than a couple of million quid, old chap. So perhaps you'd do better with Larsons. As long as they larst, if you'll pardon the pun. And of course we won't ask you to pitch for the business.'

'Not ask us to pitch?' Harry breathed into the telephone.

'Not at all, old chap. We don't believe in that kind of nonsense. We know the best agencies in town. We'll meet and see if we can work together. See if we can get on. See if you're our kind of chaps. You know what I mean.'

'Yes... of course. When would you like to meet us?'

'How about Thursday morning, old chap? Are you free? I'm afraid it'll have to be then, because there'll be four or five of us coming, and it's the only time we can all make it for months. OK?'

'Yes, Thursday morning. Fine.'

'Let's say ten o'clock shall we? We shouldn't be more than a couple of hours. And we won't be stopping for lunch.'

'Ten o'clock's fine.'

'Naturally, we'll expect you to withdraw from the Larsons' list. If things go well I mean. If we decide to get into bed together.'

'Quite.'

'Look forward to seeing you on Thursday then. We've heard so much about you, it's going to be rather fun. My secretary will send you our team. Perhaps yours could reciprocate.'

'No problem.'

'Good show. And remember, not a dicky-bird to anyone. Understood?'

As Harry replaced the receiver he was out of breath, though he had said almost nothing. A £2 million brand from Unigamble, bluest of blue-chip clients in the land! Without a competitive pitch. Unigamble's game-plan was clear. They too had read in *Campaign* of ACM's involvement in the Larsons' pitch. They too had decided ACM were sure to win, and they did not want ACM to work for one of their competitors. Not, that is, if ACM were as good as their reputation. Hence the get-to-know-each-other meeting. Unigamble would decide for themselves whether ACM were as bright as they had been painted. And hence the lack of a competitive pitch. Unigamble were not looking for a good new agency. They simply intended to stop Larsons appointing one.

Harry, Bill and Mike discussed the situation and their initial reaction was to go hell for leather for Unigamble. A major consideration for all of them – which none of them mentioned – being that it would resolve the anonymous letter dispute without further rancour.

But the choice between Unigamble and Larsons, it transpired as they talked, was not as straightforward as it seemed at first glance. Splashasoap, together with Larsons' other brands, billed nearly £4 million. The unknown Unigamble brand billed 'less than £2 million'. In clients' euphemistic language that meant £1½ million, maybe less. And Unigamble's normal practice was to test out new agencies for two or three years before either giving them a lot more business, or dropping them flat. So it would be £4 million plays £1½ million for several years at least, and the future uncertain thereafter.

Then there was the Isaacs and Isaacs situation. Isaacs and Isaacs handled Smiley toothpaste. Smiley was of no consequence to Larsons, who were not involved in the toothpaste market. But Unigamble were, in a big way. Taking Unigamble business would negate the possibility of a deal with Isaacs and Isaacs. And Stan had telephoned only that morning, to apologise for finishing their meeting so hastily, and to stress his enthusiasm to press ahead.

Anyway, they unanimously agreed, they must unquestionably aim for both for the present, since they had won neither yet. If Unigamble offered them business, they would decide once they knew which brand they were being given, what its true billings were, what its prospects seemed to be, and what they felt about the whole thing.

As Harry put it: 'While they're deciding whether they want to get into bed with us, we will be deciding whether or not we fancy them as sugar daddies.'

None of which could he explain to Paul O'Reilly, looking so pert, so diffident, so pretty in front of him. But he wanted to be as helpful as he dared. 'Well it's not true we've won Splashasoap. Far from it. In fact we've been suspecting it's *us* has been set up, and that Larsons have intended to leave the business with Pendletons all along. They're a very conservative company, Larsons. Don't like change. They're giving Pendletons a sharp boot where it hurts, that's all.'

'Are you sure?'

'No. Seems likely, though. You've probably not met old Peter Dalrymple, but ACM isn't his speed at all. And Digby's just a self-seeking smart arse. We're not right for them, and they probably know it. Clients often use agencies like us as stalking horses, to put the fear of God into their existing shops. They put us on their short lists without the slightest intention of giving us their business. Drives us wild. We can't always spot them. And anyway, we sometimes win against the odds. That might happen with Larsons but I doubt it.' Harry gazed at Paul again and wondered whether to admit he had lied, had no dinner engagement, was free as a lusty bird all evening.

'So you think it's all rumours? About people getting fired and all?'

'How can I tell, Paul? I don't work at Pendletons. My guess is they've drawn up a contingency plan against the worst happening. That's what big agencies usually do.'

'So me and Tom and the others won't get the push unless Larsons goes?'

'Probably not. But I'm only guessing.'

'Can we join ACM then? If we get the push?'

'I'd . . . I'd sooner you didn't.'

'But . . . but we'll be unemployed.'

'I know.' Harry moved across to Paul, kissed him lightly, and took his hand. 'I'm sorry. But it would be stupid. For both of us. If the worst happens I'll make a few phone calls, and get you some interviews.'

'What will I say to Tom, then?'

Harry ruffled the boy's ridiculous green hair and kissed him again swiftly on the ear. 'You'll think of something. Now I've got to go out. I really must.'

Winning Unigamble might not be an immediate financial bonanza but it would solve many problems, he thought, as he led Paul to the door, and gave his hand an affectionate farewell squeeze.

'God knows what it means, if anything at all,' Chris Beaumont addressed the assembled gang, waiting in the Pendletons' boardroom to hear Greg Hamilton deliver the populace's judgment on Tom Nathan and Paul O'Reilly's campaign. Tom and Paul were present, naturally, as was Bernie Barnstaple, who had already confidently predicted the outcome of

Hamilton's researches. Flora Thompson and Simon Booth were sitting together. Having discovered that Des Digby was keen on Tom and Paul Flora prayed that Hamilton's research results would be positive. Simon, the remaining traces of his bruises having been the butt of Tom Nathan's ribaldry that morning, prayed that they wouldn't. Neither the Vicar nor Dave Horrell had put in an appearance, both claiming important prior engagements.

'Dalrymple offered no explanation,' Chris continued, 'but said his Chairman would be attending all three agency presentations, with him and Digby. It somehow seemed impertinent to ask why, so I didn't. It castrates Peter's role as decision maker. On the other hand it stresses the importance Larsons place on the decision. I've only met the Chairman twice before in my life. I'm sure he thinks advertising agencies are well below the salt. Like printers and plastic tube manufacturers. Chaps who do awfully useful jobs, but who you don't sully your hands with. Anyway Dalrymple said that in view of his Chairman's attendance there was a three-line whip on me being present on the great day. Since it never crossed my mind not to be—Yes, ask someone to bring him up,' Chris finished as a call on the telephone announced Greg Hamilton's arrival in reception.

Only Simon and Bernie Barnstaple had met Greg Hamilton before, and Bernie greeted him, to his obvious surprise, like an old and treasured friend. The others, as Simon had predicted, were more than a little disconcerted by Hamilton's appearance. They had not expected London's leading psychological market researcher to look like anything in particular, but they were nonetheless amazed he looked as he did. From the gap between his trouser bottoms and his shoes, right up to the greasy strands of hair that crossed his pate, his appearance proclaimed that its owner did not care about it much.

As director of research and planning, it was Bernie Barnstaple's job to open the proceedings, which he did briefly – but far from briefly enough, Chris thought – as he openly indicated to Hamilton his personal distate for the campaign. Hamilton, however, who was consulting his notes with the air of a man who had never seen them before, seemed oblivious of Bernie's proselytising.

When Bernie finally finished there was a further pause, stretching into an embarrassing silence, before Hamilton began to speak in what Simon had described as his mid-Atlantic accent, but which Chris could have sworn had a touch of Viennese mixed in somewhere.

'Perhaps I must begin by explaining the methodology we have employed on this occasion. I myself carried out ten depth interviews, lasting approximately ninety minutes each, with housewives who were aware of liquid soaps but had never bothered to use one. All aged twenty-five to forty-nine in the C1C2 social classes. My assistant, Dr Hilda Bettelheim, carried out eleven similar interviews. We then compared findings. In this way we seek to obviate the danger of a single researcher's subjectivity. As it turned out – and this occurs rarely in my experience – Dr Bettelheim's conclusions and my own coincided remarkably closely. So that although the sample is small, I think you may be confident that it is robust.'

The sample, Chris mused as Hamilton spoke, was of far less importance than his phraseology, and his confident, commanding tone of voice. Like a witch-doctor, what he said was probably of less importance than the way he said it.

'We must begin, naturally, by considering the act of washing. Washing, as we all know, is one of humanity's most basic activities. While not perhaps everyone aspires to the heights of dirt-free, germ-free, odour-free, bacteria-free hygiene that are socially demanded in the United States, I know of no society in the world, no matter how primitive, in which washing does not play a vital role – a role that is indeed frequently ritualised. Consider Baptism. Or how we talk of "washing our sins away". The Moslems wash ritually before praying, the Jews wash ritually before eating. I merely stress, as you all know already, for sure, that washing is too fundamental a human activity for changes to be undertaken lightly.'

Maybe all the others knew all this before, each of his audience thought guiltily, but I didn't.

'And while mentioning the United States, where as you all know liquid soaps are widely in use, I should stress that America is, by virtue of its historical culture, a nation of change. Deep in Americans' subconscious they know that their very existence came about as a result of cataclysmic change. So naturally, to them change promises improvement. Particularly in matters as fundamental as sex, eating, drinking, and washing. Novelty is all. That is why – I hazard a guess, if I may – the Americans have devised the widest variety of ill-functioning shower fittings that it is possible to imagine. All are different, none work. But that is by-the-by. In contrast Britain, as we all know, is a nation of status quo. Our past is our glory. Our present is enfeebled. So all change threatens.'

What bollocks, thought Tom Nathan with uncharacteristic patriotism. We Brits are more inventive, more radical, and for that matter own more videos than the damn Yankees. How does that make us so conservative?

'In certain matters – we may take leisure as an example – we regard change as trivial. We even welcome it. Washing is more fundamental. It is an activity not lightly to be tampered with. It is against this background that we must view the introduction of liquid soaps into the UK. And the problems are compounded, perhaps exponentially, by two further difficulties of which you will be aware. First, you have not so far told housewives why they should make this psychological upheaval in their washing routine. Second – and I view this as a minor difficulty, which cannot be ignored nonetheless – the price of Splashasoap is high. This would be unimportant as the cost is still trivial and would be seen to be so if housewives saw a true raison d'être for the brand.'

What bollocks, thought Paul O'Reilly. Why don't he get on with it: what did they think of the ad?

'We must now come to housewives' perceptual differences between bar and liquid soaps. A psychoanalytic diagnosis suggests a penile/semen dichotomy, especially in view of the way liquid soap is ejaculated from its container. Yes, the language of *hard* bars and *squirts* of liquid lends support to this hypothesis. We should then say that bar soaps, as erect penises, are desirable, while liquid soaps, as semen – despite modern contraception and so on – threaten pregnancy and are to be avoided.'

What bollocks, thought Flora Thompson. How does he get away with such cheap Freudian codswallop?

'However both Dr Bettelheim and myself view this as a naïve Freudian diagnosis, and although some of the phrases housewives use,' he searched hurriedly through his notes, 'for example, "I like the hard feel of it", or, "it makes a sticky mess, which I can't stand" reveal subconscious evidence in its support, we do not believe it leads to the core of the problem. Copulation is here probably an irrelevance. Our diagnosis is quite different. It is a matter of power.'

What bollocks, even Chris now thought. It will be simplistic Adlerianism, instead of simplistic Freudianism, but simplistic all the same.

'This is not an especially profound diagnosis. Indeed it is refreshingly simple. Hard soaps offer housewives the power to control their washing environment, while liquid soaps, being runny and uncontrollable, are uncertain. This is partly a matter of history, partly a matter of physical form. The housewife feels herself to be master – perhaps I mean mistress! – of the bar of soap, but feels no such power over liquid soap. It is revealed in such language as "I know where I am with a bar of soap", or "it sometimes squirts all over the place", and "because you can't control the squirts, you get what the manufacturer wants, not what you want yourself." In today's society the desire of emancipated women to control their own environment, their destiny, is profound. Do I make myself clear?'

'Oh yes,' answered Simon Booth enthralled, while the others nodded their heads with varying degrees of enthusiasm.

'Now that, you must understand, is at the subconscious level. At the conscious level housewives can't perceive a real benefit from liquid soap. So we are meeting neither their emotional nor their rational needs. Whereas to be successful we must meet both. In other words we need a logico-psychological proposition. So at last we come to the advertising you have created, and pose the question. Does it provide such a proposition? Excuse me, do you have a glass of milk?'

'I'm sure we can find one,' Chris Beaumont replied,

instructing Simon to do so, while Greg Hamilton stopped and studied his notes again, unwilling to proceed until his sustenance arrived. He seemed to have far more notes than he needed, and was rather secretive about them, guarding them against anyone else's scrutiny.

'The answer to my question, I'm afraid, is yes and no,' he eventually re-started, invigorated by the liquid nourishment, 'so let us consider the positive points first. Undoubtedly the strongest single feature is the lightning. The lightning signifies an important change – something of great moment has occurred. The housewives understand the symbolism. They accept it, respect it. It's indeed crucial if they are to change their time-honoured washing traditions. Especially the final lightning exploding the pack. Excellent.'

What bollocks, now thought Bernie Barnstaple. The man is patently a charlatan.

'Second, you will remember the commercial is set in the Cotswolds. Perfect. That makes Splashasoap both new *and* acceptable. Purest British heritage. Ideal. And finally the rain. This too is good. It says moisture, and purity, and cleanliness. All the essential imagery. And were you to leave it there – a pretty girl walking through the English countryside in the rain, with the occasional bolt of lightning which she confidently, masterfully ignores – you would have, I suggest to you, exquisite communication at the subconscious level. But, as we all know, we cannot leave it there. For where is the product, where is the redemption?'

And where is all this shit leading us? wondered Tom Nathan, gratified by what Hamilton had said so far, but aware from his tone of voice that there were troubles ahead.

As if in need of further energy before returning to his Herculean task, Hamilton drained his glass of milk at one long gulp, and emitted a tiny burp. 'So now we come to the nub of the problem. The fall from grace. The fall is the end. It is catastrophic. Falling in mud evokes powerful fears, and a mere liquid soap is not nearly sufficient to dissolve them. How, the housewives worry, will she cope socially when her clothes are muddy? What if she meets somebody important? What about her legs and tights? Maybe she got mud on her face, what then of her make-up? The incident sets up resonances which are too strong. It must be deleted.'

'But,' Tom Nathan spoke after a thoughtful pause, 'if she doesn't get her hands muddy, why does she need to wash?'

'Indeed. That I cannot answer. Remember the psychology of the situation. It is a matter of power. By making her fall you make her powerless. Then you provide her with a product over which she feels also powerless. At the subconscious level it is a nightmare. My respondents, as Dr Bettelheim's, were deeply disturbed by the incident. Deeply disturbed.'

The room fell into silence for what seemed like an age, while all the Pendletons' people thought about the mire into which they had fallen.

'How about the script?' Tom Nathan eventually asked. 'You've not mentioned the words. Or the slogan.'

'No difficulties there . . . ' Greg Hamilton flipped quickly through his voluminous notes. 'The housewives fully accept the moisturising argument at the rational level. Though they feel the slogan "A Smashin' Soap" to be on the ordinary side. It could, they pointed out, be used about any product: a smashin' toothpaste, a smashin' car . . . no, maybe not a smashin' car.' The small man laughed for the first time, but none of the others joined him.

'Also Dr Bettelheim found, I see, though not myself, that many of her respondents thought it condescending. Particularly the missing "g". Dr Bettelheim is very sensitive to such matters, you know. Is there anything else I can tell you?'

No, one and all agreed, they had had their fill. And with only thirty-six hours to go before the presentation, with half a commercial and a condescending slogan on the ordinary side, what were they to do now?

IX
Presentations

'How did it go?'
'How d . . . d . . . do you think it went?'
'That tall one didn't like us!'
'Och, that was only a pose. He was trying to look tough. The one with the funny wee ears was on our side.'
'F . . . f . . . funny ears?'
'Wee ears with huge red lobes. Did you not notice them?'
Bill McAndrew's quirky perceptions never failed to astound his colleagues.
'Was that John Fairmount?'
'No, Fairmount was the one with the stoop. Wee ears was Tommy Theobald.'
'Well, I didn't notice his ears but I think he liked us. The tall one didn't though. It wasn't a pose. He's against us. For some reason.'
'He's not important anyway. The key guy was Fairmount, and he seemed friendly OK.'
'Well the tall one – was he Wilkinson? – was definitely gunning for us. That question he asked, "Do you think your agency is mature enough to handle an account of our size and complexity?" What a berk! What did he expect us to answer? No, Mr Wilkinson, now you come to mention it I suppose we are a bit immature. Babyish, really.'
Messrs Adams, Coventry and McAndrew were dissecting their just ended presentation to Unigamble. At least four of the five Unigamble visitors had listened attentively to Harry's sales spiel, had acclaimed Bill McAndrew's creativity, had enthused over Mike Coventry's astute analyses of ACM's clients' marketing problems. An outsider might have expected, from the ebullience of the Unigamble team's reactions, that they were about to appoint ACM to handle their entire multi-million pound account on the spot. A more experienced

observer would have recognised that Unigamble executives almost always behaved enthusiastically on such occasions: they feel it to be good manners.

Most of Unigamble's questions had been ritualistic: 'Who would personally be responsible for our business? How much of the principals' time would we get? How will you keep up standards as you grow bigger? What are your long-term ambitions? Have you lost any accounts since you started up? What do you think are the benefits of multinational, as against local, campaigns?' And to each in turn, Adams, Coventry and McAndrew provided well-rehearsed answers. Only three questions momentarily fazed them: Wilkinson's inquiry about their maturity; another asking which of them were university graduates ('I never expected to hear that asked after I was twenty-one' Harry Adams later said, having ditched school at the age of fifteen, and having embarrassingly fluffed the answer); and a question from John Fairmount – which they all later admitted to admiring – on what they thought would be the most difficult or unpleasant aspect of working with Unigamble, were they to be appointed.

None of them had rushed in with a reply and so the questioner had repeated his query: 'We know you'll have thought of lots of good things to say about working with us, but surely you must have the itsy-bitsiest of worries? No business relationship is all sweetness and light, not even working with Unigamble!'

General laughter, then more silence. Bill and Mike looked towards Harry, willing him to take the lead. 'That's a fast ball,' he eventually replied, 'and we don't really know enough about you to answer it. We don't even know which brand we'll be working on.'

'Come off it, Mr Adams, you can do better than that.'

Harry laughed. 'I was just going to. Well, everyone knows Unigamble are a marvellous client,' he chose his words carefully, 'and that you are demanding but fair. You don't work to formulas, like lots of large advertisers. You encourage creativity. But you do tend to have a reputation for moving rather slowly. For researching every tiny decision. For paralysis by analysis.'

He had hit the right note: the Unigamble people grinned. It was acceptable criticism.

'And being new, we're rather impatient. So I foresee a bit of conflict on that score. Which no doubt you'll win!'

'Anything else?' Everyone was still smiling happily.

'Only that you're famous for having a rather strict attitude to competitive accounts. Once we work with you we'll be barred from lots of other clients.'

'You're thinking of Larsons?'

'Among others. But that's a small price to pay. For the benefits of being a Unigamble agency.'

Now, as they analysed and re-analysed the event, the three of them returned to slagging off the one member of the Unigamble group they were convinced was against them.

'N . . . not just babyish, Mr Wilkinson. In . . . infantile,' Mike Coventry capped Harry Adams' earlier remark.

'What's the difference?' Harry chuckled.

'Infantile's more b . . . babyish than babyish.'

'And Wilkinson's brain is blunt as a rusty razor.'

'He's thicker than two short planks.'

'Did you s . . . see how many notes he took? F . . . five or six pages' worth. They're the worst clients in the world. The ones that are d . . . d . . . diligent, and dumb with it.'

'I believe Metternich said much the same about army officers,' Harry agreed.

'Och, Wilkinson's not important. He's just a clunt.'

'C . . . c . . . c . . . clunt?'

'A cross between a client and a— '

There was a sharp rap on the boardroom door and the visitor came in immediately, without waiting for an invitation. The room went coldly silent.

'Hallo, Mr Wilkinson,' said Harry drily.

'I left my briefcase,' Wilkinson replied, 'sorry. There it is. Thank you so much for your presentation.' He collected his case and departed in an instant, leaving Adams, Coventry and McAndrew aghast.

They couldn't be sure whether he had heard what they had been saying, but feared the worst.

'I could murder myself. The only infallible rule about new

client presentations is never to say a word until you're absolutely sure they've left the building. Not a dicky-bird, as Fairmount would say,' Harry chastised himself as the telephone warbled.

'I'll take it,' he replied when the telephonist asked if calls were now to be put through. 'It's Greg Hamilton. D'you want to talk to him, Mike?'

Slumped in his chair, untypically wearing a dark suit in honour of Unigamble's visit, Mike Coventry shook his head.

'Greg? It's Harry. Yes, we'd better meet tomorrow. Can you give me the top line results quickly . . . thanks . . . Yes . . . yes, I see . . . Well I don't think we Brits are as conservative as all that . . . OK, maybe about washing, maybe you're right . . . I thought the Moslems only took their shoes off? . . . Penis and semen substitutes? You must be joking, Greg. . . . Oh . . . yes, that makes a lot more sense . . . so what about our concept . . . oh . . . really . . . they don't want it to be young and lively then? Not even the younger housewives? . . . You mean the present pack and positioning are reassuring and comfortable . . . so our attempt to appeal to the young market is right out, in your opinion? . . . Well . . . what about the other approaches we put into the research? What about the moisturising concept? . . . They liked that, did they? . . . younger as well as older? . . . Surprises me . . . You know best, Greg. . . . You know we always take your advice . . . OK then, get your secretary to fix a time with Janet. . . . Thanks, Greg, see you tomorrow.'

With evident dismay, Harry put down the telephone. 'We'd better hope Wilkinson didn't hear us,' he said to his two partners, 'because Hamilton says our attempt to give Splashasoap a younger image is completely misconceived. That's not its problem. Mind you, I didn't get what the problem is exactly. It's to do with modern emancipated women wanting power over their environment, apparently.'

'B . . . b . . . but what's that to do with Splashasoap?'

'God knows. Greg's coming in tomorrow to explain. What's worse is that Pendletons' moisturising approach seems right. Though I can't see how that's got much to do with the power of emancipated women either.'

From having been manic less than thirty minutes previously, Harry was now plugged into depression. 'He didn't research Pendletons' crappy creative work, though. Did he?'

'No. We only asked him to examine the basic concept. Which seems to be good. Now we've got a couple of days to change tack and start again.'

'I say we ignore him. He's not infallible.'

'He's the best psychological researcher in town.'

'Well I say fuck him,' Bill McAndrew responded unyieldingly.

'Maybe we'll g . . . g . . . get Unigamble.'

'Not if Mr Clunt-Wilkinson has anything to do with it,' Harry demurred.

'I've got it,' enthused small Paul, 'she's walking in the rain and this fella gallops up on a white stallion, lifts her on it, and they gallop off through the wood. That's got a bit of romance, anyway.'

' 'Ow do we get Splashasoap into it?'

'In . . . in the pack shot, I suppose.'

'We gotta do more than that, you little Celtic schmuck.'

The last-minute delivery of Greg Hamilton's bombshell had resulted in Tom Nathan and Paul O'Reilly working overnight to reformulate their commercial. They were doing so with little enthusiasm, repeatedly pointing out to anyone within ear shot, and to each other, that many of advertising's greatest campaigns had failed in research, that the public never accepted radical creativity initially – 'Remember the Impressionists . . . nobody liked them at first either . . . nor the Avis "we try harder" campaign' – that Greg Hamilton's sample had been too small to be statistically reliable, and that nobody at Pendletons had any balls, which was why they allowed themselves to be steamrollered by market research, and was why it would never be a really creative agency – 'Frank Lowe would've told that phoney little psychologist to stuff 'is crackpot theories up 'is anal orientation.'

While they were working, Chris Beaumont, Flora Thompson and Bernie Barnstaple were disputing how to handle the presentation of Greg Hamilton's research findings. Indubitably his basic analysis of the market should be exposed to Larsons. But should Pendletons also reveal their original commercial, admit that it had been significantly wrong, and trace its development and correction? (Presuming Tom and Paul succeeded in correcting it.) Or would it be better to censor Hamilton's results and present the final commercial as though it had been created on the basis of his analysis? Bernie Barnstaple wanted to tell the whole truth; Flora Thompson said that would be far too confusing, that Larsons would never be able to follow what had happened, and would somehow get the wrong end of the stick. Chris Beaumont sided with Flora.

Around the building secretaries were typing, re-typing and re-re-typing media recommendations and schedules; projection slides were being made, re-made, re-re-made because they were the wrong size, or wrongly spelt, or out of focus, or simply grubby; mini-rehearsals were in progress in different rooms and Simon Booth, attempting to control the project but lacking the authority to do so, scampered frenetically from office to office, pestering all concerned. Meanwhile the advertising campaign, upon which this shaky house of cards was being erected, was still virtually non-existent.

'This is better,' said Tom after a long, pregnant silence. 'She sees two little kids, a boy and girl, about six or seven and they're all soaked and muddy and lovable and she takes their 'ands - so she gets muddy - and leads them to safety somewhere. I don't know where yet. Then she washes 'er 'ands, and we're 'ome and dry - even if she's not!'

'Nope . . .' Paul disagreed pensively, 'how would you be knowing they weren't her own kids? Anyway people would get angry about their parents, letting them get soaked like that. The NSPCC would be down on us like a ton a bricks.'

'Balls.'

'I'm telling yer. We'll never get it past the IBA copy censors.'

'They fuck up all really great creative ideas, those bastards, but still.'

'Once more they lapsed into silence. It was now well past eleven o'clock and everyone else had gone home. The deserted building felt hollow, abnormally quiet, spooky: advertising agencies are meant to be busy and clamorous, it's unnatural for them to be hushed and still.

'This 'ole thing's bloody ridiculous,' Tom grumbled, not for the first time. 'If they wanna believe the bleeding research then the 'ole idea is no good and it's back to the drawing board time. We can't stick a different ending on to the same beginning. We'll end up with the proverbial camel, the 'orse designed by a committee. It's a typical Pendletons' fuck-up. Let's 'ave a bit of this, a bit of that, a bit of the other. I wouldn't mind a bit of the other, come to think of it.'

'Nor would I, for that matter.'

'You, you paddy pooftah? 'Oo do you fancy, then? Snotty Simon? 'E was probably a lovely little bumboy at 'Arrow.'

Paul O'Reilly froze. His homosexuality had never before been mentioned. Never. He felt instantly threatened, terrified. He must have been seen, somewhere, with somebody. In a gay bar? With Harry Adams that night at The Queensbury? People must have been gossiping. Behind his back. What would they have been saying? A secret part of him had been exposed and he was frightened. All straights detest gays no matter how much they deny it. 'And . . . and who says . . . anything about me being gay?' he asked very quietly.

'Nobody. Don't worry, you stupid green-haired mick. Nobody else suspects. Not as far as I know. Nobody's ever said anything. But I've been working with you for nearly two years, so you could 'ardly expect to keep it secret from me. And I don't give a monkeys.'

Paul looked at Tom's bushy, bearded face. His eyes were affectionate, generous, and tired. 'Come on,' he said, 'let's crack this bastard and get some kip.'

Silence returned, but Paul found it difficult to concentrate on Splashasoap. How long had Tom known, he wondered. How could he be sure Tom had never told anyone else . . . ?

'This is it!' Tom leapt from his chair and began to pace around the tiny office. 'She sees this idyllic Cotswold cottage, in the rain, maybe in soft focus, like a dream, an' she knocks on the door, and this wizened old crone opens it . . . no, she'd better be a lovable little old biddy or Obergruppenführer Beaumont won't approve . . . and then she goes in and lights a fire for the old biddy, gets 'er 'ands grubby in the process, the biddy gives 'er a pack of Splashasoap and . . . nar, it's rubbish,'

Tom throttled his own creation at birth, 'it's shit, two C's in a K in a Cotswold cottage. Forget it.' They were beginning to feel insecure, queasy. Like all creative people desperately searching for an idea, and working to a tight deadline, they could not be sure that it would come. It had in the past, every time. But this time ... it might not happen. Original ideas can't be manufactured to order, like sausages.

'God, and I'm exhausted.'

'You know, Pauly, we've gotta get out of this place, and quick. We can't create great ads this way. It's fuckin' nonsense, yer know. They've got no idea 'ow to get award-winnin' stuff done. If we don't get out soon we'll become shitheads like everyone else 'ere.'

'I'd love to win a DADA gold,' Paul murmured wistfully, 'to go up there, in the spotlight, at the Grosvenor House, with all the creatives in London watching, and clapping, and cheering, and jealous.'

'You shall, my boy. *We* shall. But not in this cesspit. We're as creative as Webster, and 'Egarty, and Trotty any day of the week. We've just gotta get somewhere where they recognise great creativity when they see it. Pity we've not heard from ACM.'

'Oh, didn't I tell you? Fred phoned. She said it's all off there,' Paul lied nervously.

'Fuck!' Tom swore in exasperation, 'fuck! fuck! fuck!'

Despite which despondency, and despite the impossibility of solving the problem, they cracked it shortly after four o'clock that morning, fell asleep in their office, and presented the new solution to Chris Beaumont et al a few hours later. It was greeted with acclaim (and relief) by all concerned. Paul and Tom were instructed to transform it from rough scribbles to an animatic rough commercial without delay.

'Can I speak to Peter Dalrymple?' Harry Adams tried hard to choke back the exaltation in his voice, 'Yes, it's rather urgent. If he could be interrupted please.'

Peter's normally kindly voice was gruff when eventually he came to the telephone. He had been working through computer print-outs with Larsons' Production Director for the umpteenth time, at the Chairman's request, estimating Splashasoap's sales and profits over the next five years at varying levels of advertising expenditure. All the projections were gloomy, some more gloomy than others. Being summoned from his calculations by Harry Adams did not improve his demeanour.

'What can I do for you?'

'Sorry to interrupt your meeting, Mr Dalrymple, but I thought I should let you know immediately that we – Adams Coventry McAndrews – are pulling out of this Splashasoap race.' The glee in his voice was difficult to disguise. It was very rare for an advertising agency to be able to turn down a multi-million pound account, and he felt superior, arrogant, cocky.

'Pulling out? What do you mean?'

'We've been appointed by one of your competitors.'

'Our competitors?'

'Unigamble. They've asked us to handle Fresko, and we've accepted, I'm afraid.'

Dalrymple was distraught. He had been relying on ACM to find a new future for Splashasoap. He had little confidence in Pendletons' ability to do so, still less in Des's second-rate friends at GOB. 'But . . . but surely this is unethical behaviour, Mr Adams. We were expecting you to present for our business tomorrow.'

'That's why I was so anxious to get through to you. I'm afraid it's all happened rather quickly.'

'Rather quickly! You've been working on Splashasoap for several weeks now. And we have provided you with a good deal of confidential information. You cannot behave in this way, you know. I can't agree to your proposal.'

Harry was nonplussed. He had expected a thirty-second 'goodbye and good-luck' conversation. Dalrymple was more senile than he had thought. 'I'm sorry,' he said slowly, 'but the decision is ours not yours, Mr Dalrymple. And I don't agree that it is in any way unethical. ACM was one of three agencies pitching for your business. So we had a one in three chance of winning. Whereas Unigamble is a bird in the hand. And a very prestigious one too, as you well know.'

Peter Dalrymple began to feel his chest constrict, his vision blur, but he was not ill. 'But Fresko's a dying brand,' he pressed on, 'whereas liquid soaps are the thing of the future. Are you sure you'll be making the right decision?'

Harry now had no wish to continue what had, turned out to be an awkward conversation. 'We're not making the decision, Mr Dalrymple. We've made it. It's final. So I should like to thank you for considering us and— '

'Hold on, Mr Adams. Supposing . . . supposing we offered you our business straightaway. Without the competitive pitch, I mean. It's a bigger account than Fresko you know. Considerably bigger.'

Harry was stunned: he and his partners had all along suspected – as he had told Paul O'Reilly – that the business was destined to stay at Pendletons, that the competition was phoney. That view had weighed heavily in their decision to accept Unigamble and ditch Larsons. 'Is . . . is that a definite offer, Mr Dalrymple?'

'No . . . not at this stage. I should need to discuss it with my Chairman and . . . and so on. But there's no point in me doing so if, as you say, your decision is taken and the matter closed.'

'Well . . . ' Harry did not disagree with Peter Dalrymple. Larsons was twice as big an account, in the short run at least; Fresko's sales had been declining, probably irreversibly, for years. And the Unigamble v. Isaacs and Isaacs clash was still in the back of his mind. ' . . . well . . . my colleagues and I would obviously consider your proposition seriously, if you make it to us. But it would have to be in the next hour, as a press release about our appointment is going out from Unigamble later today.'

'Leave it to me, Mr Adams, I'll be back to you shortly.'

Gilbernetti, Orr and Burton's presentation was going surprisingly well. With unaccustomed thoroughness the GOB team had rehearsed the event not just once but twice, from start to finish.

Their level of confidence was uncharacteristically high. None of them could conceive of the agency going bust. For the company suddenly to be bankrupt, to vanish, for all of them to be out of work and loaded with debts, with bank guarantees they could not meet and mortgages they could not repay – it was beyond comprehension, too horrifying to contemplate. The gods could not be so brutal. Not even to a determined pessimist like James Orr. So they were going to win. Everything was going their way. Especially ACM's astonishing withdrawal from the joust, of which Peter Dalrymple had informed them the previous evening.

Hal Burton had opened the proceedings with an analysis of the soap market, tracing the disappointingly slow growth of liquid soap sales – particularly when compared with the USA – and had put forward several hypothetical explanations for the phenomenon. Differing washing habits? Not really. Hardness of water? Certainly not. Traditional British conservatism? A symptom, not a cause. Differing attitudes to skin care? No evidence to support that, much the reverse. When every possible hypothesis had been analysed. Hal concluded, the only one which made sense was the most obvious: price. It was, he said, to flatter Peter Dalrymple, a perfect marketing example of Occam's razor: the simplest explanation was the best. Liquid soaps were at least six times as costly, per wash, in the UK as in the USA. That was the beginning and end of it. There was no need for profound or convoluted psychological analyses.

So it was the job of advertising to justify the price. How? By making liquid soap – or rather Splashasoap – a smart, premium quality brand which was worth paying the extra for. There was, Hal insisted, as he flashed his final two slides on the screen, no alternative.

'So the creative strategy we recommend,' he read the words off the screen: 'To communicate Splashasoap as the smart, modern way to wash, which is worth paying more for.'

He had only slightly re-phrased Irving's original effort. Hal flashed up his last slide, 'And the desired consumer response we require— '

'Desired consumer response?' broke in Larsons' Chairman, who until then had remained silent, not to say somnolent. 'What the hell's that?'

The Chairman, Hal Burton thought, is the very epitome of old-fashioned British top management, right down to his Old

Etonian tie, his fob watch, his silk top-pocket handkerchief and elegantly curled grey moustache.

'Well,' Hal tried to keep in mind that he was addressing Larson's Chairman and not a half-wit, 'it doesn't really matter what we put into an advertisement...' he paused for thought.

'Doesn't it?' The Chairman was puzzled. 'I'd have rather thought it did.'

'No, it's what people – consumers, viewers, readers – *take out* of the advertisement that counts. We can throw in everything, including the kitchen sink. But it is what *they* notice, remember, are influenced by, that matters. Not what we say, but how they respond.'

'Brevity is the soul of wit, and so on. Is that what you're saying?' the Chairman asked.

'In a way, yes. Well, not exactly.' Hal wished to labour the point no longer. 'We write down a sort of definition of how we hope consumers will respond when they see the advertising. And we call it the desired consumer response. Advertising jargon, I suppose. Anyway this is it for Splashasoap.' He once again read from the screen: 'Desired consumer response: "Smart women seem to be using Splashasoap, so if I want to be fashionable I ought to try it too."'

'It's not a frock;' said the Chairman as Hal finished, 'that makes it sound like the latest in Paris haute couture! It's only soap y'know.'

'The desired consumer response is a device,' Peter Dalrymple interceded, he hoped judiciously, 'to help the agency define the communications objectives for the advertising. It's one of their professional techniques, that's all.'

'I see,' the Chairman said, palpably failing to do so, 'as long as they've not muddled up Splashasoap with Gucci.'

'No way, sir,' Irving Gilbernetti leapt in, mentally editing several Gucci analogies from his forthcoming dissertation, 'but if I may begin to present the creative work now....' He got up and switched off the projector to avoid any further discussion of the offending desired consumer response slide. 'We do strongly feel that the Splashasoap pack ain't right. I mean, it's a neat pack OK. But not for a premium, expensive product. Like Splashasoap.'

Irving proceeded to present to Peter Dalrymple, Des Digby and Larsons' Chairman the work that had been received so warmly by his colleagues a few days previously. The reactions of the Larsons trio were more muted: neither overtly enthusiastic nor overtly hostile. Polite but undemonstrative interest was the zenith of their response. Until he reached the advertisements themselves. '... and while Splashasoap's no Gucci product,' he laughed, 'we do believe you need a little advertising in the glossy monthlies to polish the image – *Vogue*, *Harpers* and so on; Hal will take you through the media schedule later –as well as the telly. So we need a neat multi-media campaign, that'll work in glossies *and* on TV. No mean challenge to an agency, you'll agree ...'

Peter Dalrymple, still smarting from the Chairman's refusal to allow him to call off the competition and award the business to ACM without further ado, looked at his colleagues and wondered what they were thinking. Des Digby was inscrutable as ever. The Chairman, he feared, probably liked what he had seen. It had been a mistake allowing the Chairman to attend the agency presentations. He should have resisted it more tenaciously. It was not a Chairman's job, he had no experience, and would be far too easily impressed.

'... so first I'm gonna show you the theme, the slogan,' Irving was continuing, 'then I'm gonna show you how it works out in TV and in the magazines. OK? This is it.' He lifted a board on which had been typeset in a light sophisticated open typeface:

SPLASHASOAP

NOW IT'S TOMORROW TODAY

'Don't get it,' said the Chairman.

Dalrymple shot him a frustrated, withering glance. It had been a terrible mistake to bring him.

Irving was disappointed, but continued valiantly. 'So wait till you see it in the ads,' he said, 'here. I'll show you the telly commercial first.'

The commercial was set in a futuristic kitchen in the middle of which a housewife, in an elegant silver lame dress, reclined on a glass chaise-longue and gave instructions to everything in the room via a hand-held remote control widget. The taps turned on and off, as did the microwave, and the dishwasher; the crockery travelled by tiny conveyor belt, at her behest, along the shelves. An electronic bleep sounded, and she switched on a video screen above her head with the remote control to reveal a milkman, outside her door, dressed like John Glenn landing on the moon, and carrying a crate of parabolic-shaped milk bottles. She pressed the control again to bring the words 'Two demi-litres today please, Bert' on to the screen, then switched off the video and opened a distant can of catfood for her silver-white cat, which naughtily pushed its food on to the floor. She got up, nimbly replaced it on the cat's plate, and went to the sink to wash her hands with . . . Splashasoap. For the first ten seconds the sound-track was electronic music, then a mellifluous male voice spoke: 'Even when everything else is done for you, there will be some things you'll have to do for yourself. Like washing your hands. Then it will be nice to know you've got the most advanced type of soap in the world . . . to hand. Splashasoap. Now it's tomorrow today.'

    The Chairman was patently pleased, as was the inscrutable Des Digby. Even Peter Dalrymple had to admit to himself that it was good. It was sheer imagery, of course. No product benefit. No reason to buy. He would need to tinker with that, but it would be simple enough to insert a moisturising claim, or something, into the voice-over. They had been a bit indulgent with the electronic music. There were plenty of seconds to spare. But the visual was strong, and original, and relevant, and the slogan was excellent in context.

    The magazine ads, lifted directly from the commercial, were less impressive. None of the Larsons team anyway believed that advertising in glossy magazines was a good idea for Splashasoap, and so there was a heated argument during which the GOB team defended their proposal enthusiastically until – and it didn't take too long – they saw the irrefutable logic of their prospective client's argument.

    'Going back to the commercial for a moment,' said the Chairman, 'ought the milkman really to be called "Bert"? Sounds a bit silly to me.'

'All British milkmen are called Bert,' said Irving emphatically.

'But surely they won't be in the future? Oughtn't he to be called Zircon or something?'

'But that's the joke, sir.' Irving looked wounded.

'Didn't make me laugh. Just seemed silly to me.'

'It's a very good point.' James Orr glowered at Irving, 'we'll certainly consider it very carefully.'

'On a different subject,' asked Des Digby to display his professionalism, 'wouldn't it be an extremely expensive commercial to make?'

'Nope,' Irving replied untruthfully, 'it's a cast of one and a simple set-build. What could be cheaper?' (There was no point in arguing about the production cost until after they had won the account.)

Neither Des nor Peter believed him (but there was no point in arguing about the production cost until after GOB had been appointed), and both they and the Chairman left the presentation greatly encouraged by what they had seen.

Chris Beaumont had just begun to introduce the Pendletons' team to the three visitors when the telephone rang in the conference room.

'It's for you,' Simon Booth said to him.

'For goodness' sake!' Chris was exasperated. 'Tell them we're not taking calls. From anyone. They should know that. I'm sorry,' he apologised to Larsons' Chairman as Simon passed on the message and rang off.

'Obviously a mistake. As I was saying, I myself will introduce the presentation and present our analysis of the marketing problem – we've carried out some original and extremely significant market research, which I'll summarise' (Chris had decided Bernie Barnstaple could not be trusted to present Hamilton's research findings) 'and then our new young creative team, Tom Nathan' (dressed as scruffily as ever, much to Chris's irritation) 'and Paul O'Reilly, will show you their stunning new campaign . . . '

The telephone rang again.

'Take it off the hook,' Chris ordered.

'But it might be for one of our visitors,' Simon replied, continuing as soon as he had answered, 'it isn't though, it's for you. The police.'

'Police?' Chris walked across and took the call. '. . . I see . . . oh . . . oh God . . . yes . . . I'll be as quick as I can . . . of course.'

Having replaced the receiver Chris stared silently and unseeingly at those around him. He had taken upon himself most of the burden of the presentation and to desert it now would ensure disaster, with all that meant in terms of jobs and the agency's future, his own future, the cleaning ladies' future, Flora's future . . .

'What's happened, Christopher?' Peter Dalrymple and the Vicar were the only people he knew who used his full name.

'Couldn't we postpone the presentation?' Chris replied. 'A couple of days or so?'

'What's up?' asked the Chairman.

'It's my wife,' Chris replied in a monotone, 'she's been in a road accident. Hit by a bus. She's in intensive care. I ought to go. Her spine's badly broken.'

'Course you must,' said Peter Dalrymple, 'immediately. We'll manage.'

'Can't the presentation be postponed?' Chris asked again.

'Don't be silly. Flora will take over, won't you, Flora?' Dalrymple was insistent.

'Don't worry, we won't mark Pendletons down,' said the Chairman.

'You'll probably score a few sympathy points!' added Des Digby, with characteristic charm.

'I'd sooner postpone . . . ' Chris repeated.

'Can't be done, old chum,' the Chairman settled the matter. 'Now be on your way and let the rest of us continue. And give her our best regards when you get there.'

'She's unconscious.'

As his chauffeur sped him towards the hospital through blustery October rain, Chris's mind was suffused, confused with guilt. Throughout his career the ethics, and consequent priorities, of business life had baffled him. His wife would probably not regain consciousness for hours, the police had said. So why was he rushing to the hospital? Because no other course of action was possible. Yet losing Splashasoap would cost dozens of people their livelihoods. Though even had he stayed they might not have won . . . and what if the accident proved not to be that serious, and his wife recovered, and meanwhile Pendletons lost the business? . . . How would he explain everything to Bob Boyne? . . . . What, he wondered, would Boyne have done in the same circumstances? . . . . Stayed at the presentation no doubt . . . to be truly successful in advertising you need to be so obsessed with it that you allow nothing, nothing at all, to take precendence. . . . So many of his friends were estranged from their wives, had hardly seen their children grow up . . . job before family, or family before job? The answers given by protagonists of both sides of the argument he knew to be simplistic, naïve . . . particularly when many other people's employment depended upon your own blinkered commitment. . . . It sounded as though she might be crippled . . . it was horrific . . . how would they cope? He might have to quit Pendletons. He would certainly stop seeing Flora . . . though where was the logic in that? . . . Maybe she would die. . . .

The thought stopped him short and he felt nauseous; he wanted to retch. He opened the car window and the bitter rain flailed his face. Would he have been feeling so sickeningly guilty if he had not been carrying on with Flora? . . . He wondered how the presentation was going: Flora wouldn't be able to control it, Bernie Barnstaple and Tom Nathan would both get out of hand, quite probably start bickering about the commercial. . . . Oh hell, he shouldn't have left, it was unfair to dash all the efforts and hopes of the team on a pointless rush to her bedside about which she wouldn't even know . . . maybe he should instruct the chauffeur to turn back. . . .

The chauffeur had never before seen him muttering to himself, as he was doing when he emerged from the car, dazed and shambling, at the hospital.

'The show must go on,' said Larsons' Chairman cheerfully as the door closed behind Chris Beaumont.

'Would you like us to adjourn to another office for ten minutes while you sort yourselves out?' Peter Dalrymple offered.

'Yes, if you don't mind,' replied Flora Thompson.

'No,' replied Bernie Barnstaple simultaneously, having spotted – with Chris's departure – his opportunity.

'Yes,' chorused the Vicar.

'No,' chorused Dave Horrell.

Fortunately Simon Booth, Tom Nathan and Paul O'Reilly kept their opinions on the matter, if any, to themselves.

'Where would you like us to go?' Peter Dalrymple asked, taking his lead from Flora.

'Be quick, though,' added the Chairman, stroking his elegant moustache, ' 'fraid we've not got all day. The show must go on.'

While Simon led them to Chris Beaumont's nearby office, Flora and Bernie wrangled about who should present Greg Hamilton's research findings. Chris had told Flora the evening before that he was worried Bernie might scupper the entire presentation if he bellyached publicly about the research. Chris had been in two minds about allowing him to attend at all; but if statistical questions arose Bernie was the only person in Pendletons qualified to deal with them. None of which Flora could reveal. Moreover she had other thoughts on her mind. So Bernie won, and the Larsons entourage were recalled.

'On with the motley,' commanded the Chairman as he took his seat, and Flora, at the lectern, started her (or rather Chris Beaumont's) presentation.

Some advertising people write out and read their presentations, but Chris Beaumont was not one of them. Chris almost always spoke extempore while Albert, the Pendletons projectionist, flashed the presentation slides on to the screen from his tiny projection room. Albert was one of Pendletons' old retainers, a crotchety old thing whom Bob Boyne regularly listed for firing – 'You can work your own damn video and slides with remote control, can't you?' – but whose neck Chris had so far saved.

When younger, Chris had checked his knowledge of every

presentation the evening before, in bed, instead of counting sheep, by running through all the slides in his head; but his failing memory, the number of presentations he made, and his predilection for a couple of stiff drinks at bedtime had long ago forced him to abandon that super-efficient system. Nowadays he simply rehearsed a few times with Albert, who had learned the rhythms of his speeches, and they worked together almost telepathically. It was not a system designed to accommodate unrehearsed understudies.

Nonetheless, Flora opened the proceedings smoothly enough. Albert dimmed the lights, and she introduced Simon who reported on everything he had learned – well, perhaps not quite everything – from his store-check. For added verisimilitude photographs had been taken of the fascias of the stores he had visited, and slides flashed sequentially on to the screen behind him as he spoke – Tesco, Fine Fare, Asda, Safeway, Sainsbury's, K. Patel, stooB: fuck, the slide was upside down and back to front. It had been OK in rehearsal, he was sure.

'Obviously their Australian branch,' commented the Chairman.

'Just testing, to check you're awake.' called out Dave Horrell from somewhere in the darkened room.

'Lucky someone is,' replied a voice which sounded like Des Digby.

'Sorry about that,' said Simon, and pressed on lamely to his summary slide, which detailed Splashasoap's poor in-store display in order to shift blame for its low sales, less than utterly subtly, from Pendletons' advertising to Larsons' own sales- men.

'Well done, Simon,' Peter Dalrymple clapped, alone, 'most interesting. Are we going to be given copies of the slides?'

'Oh yes,' Flora replied as she returned to the lectern, 'I forgot to mention that at the beginning. Would you like them now?'

'No,' shouted Simon. The photocopier had broken down earlier that morning and the copies were only now, he prayed, being completed to be given to Larsons as they departed.

'Well, not yet then.' Flora was bewildered.

'We'll hand them out later,' Simon said.

'Later,' Flora agreed with her subordinate, and then paused, finding it hard to concentrate.

'So on with the motley,' said the Chairman again, much to the irritation of both Messrs Dalrymple and Digby. He seemed to be treating the agency presentations as cabaret, with the presenters as jesters, there to amuse him.

'Sorry about that,' said Flora as she re-started, though it was far from clear to anyone what she was apologising for. She began Chris Beaumont's analysis of the market, running through a mass of complex data, with which she was all too conversant, having prepared Chris's slides for him and briefed him thoroughly on their content. Entangling herself in the detail, she hip-hopped from fact to fact, from slide to slide, repeatedly referring to data from slides before, or slides following, to the consternation and confusion of her clients. Less than surprisingly, Albert was unable to follow her many trains of thought, telepathy – like cheap-flight airline tickets – being non-transferable. The Pendletons people, similarly flummoxed, hoped desperately that the clients were still following her even though they themselves were lost. It was all a little like the emperor's new clothes.

'. . . and so you can clearly see,' she ended, though none of them could, 'that there is no simple explanation of Splashasoap's failure. Your own research has shown the product is excellent, even though the pine fragrance is, shall we say, not universally, well not altogether, popular, and the price is a trifle, well, on the high side. The attitudinal studies have shown there is latent demand for liquid soaps. The concept scored well above average on the propensity-to-buy scales. Consumers' awareness of the advertising of our "gunge and grime" theme is high. Simon showed how in-store display is weak, but, of course, that's a chicken and egg problem. If its sales were stronger the stores would display it better. So what is the problem?' Flora paused to collect her thoughts.

'Don't ask us,' the Chairman growled, baffled and bored by her reiteration of old data, 'that's what we're asking you!'

'Oh . . . yes. Yes. So that's why we set the problem to the best market researcher in the country. You've probably heard of him. Greg Hamilton.'

'Who?' grunted the Chairman.

'He's . . . very famous. In market research, that is . . . Anyway we set him the problem, and Bernie Barnstaple will now report his findings.'

Flora looked around the room but Bernie Barnstaple was gone. She started to panic, but seconds later he reappeared, through the door to Albert's projection room, and strode purposefully to the lectern. Determined to avoid a further shambolic slide mix-up, and keen to make the most of his forthcoming moments in the spotlight of stardom, Bernie had decided to employ a presentation technique that he had been much impressed by at a market research conference, and he had been giving Albert instructions.

He thrust his right arm in the air, as though about to make a Nazi salute and cry '*Zieg Heil*!', but instead snapped his fingers. In response Albert clicked up the first slide and Bernie, taking off his horn-rimmed specs with his left hand and waving them like a conductor's baton to give his words added authority and emphasis, began his address. He quickly outlined the research objectives, Greg Hamilton's methodology and the sample, eschewing, Flora was relieved to register, any hint of criticism. Every few seconds he lifted his arm and snapped his fingers nimbly, and the slides changed smoothly, and at last the presentation moved forward. Bernie explained Greg's views on the ritual significance of washing, and his concept of the logico-psychological proposition.

' . . . and while Hamilton is not himself a psychoanalyst he examined the possibility that Freudian explanation . . . ' Snap. Click. On to the screen came the words 'A FREUDIAN HYPOTHESIS', discreetly avoiding Greg Hamilton's talk of erections and ejaculations. ' . . . which he rejected. . . . ' Snap, Click . . . 'SEX IS AN IRRELEVANCE', said the slide.

'Not to me it isn't,' whispered someone in the audience, probably Tom Nathan.

'Thank heaven for that,' said the Chairman firmly.

Was he responding to the slide or the whisper? Bernie wasn't waiting to find out. Snap, click. ' . . . instead Hamilton has advanced a more realistic hypothesis . . . ' he spoke over the slide reading 'TODAY'S HOUSEWIFE DEMANDS

POWER AND CONTROL'.

'Sounds like a bit of bondage there,' the voice whispered again. It had to be Nathan.

Bernie suppressed his anger and pressed on resolutely. Snap, click, snap, click.

In the audience Des Digby made a mental note to master the finger-snapping technique: it was highly effective. Very macho. Far better than pressing those wimpish little hand controls which invariably reversed the slides when you meant them to go forward.

Snap, click, snap, click.

'... so the logico-psychological proposition we require...' Bernie had reached his peroration without once undermining the research, Flora was delighted to note.

Snap, No click.

Snap, snap. Still no click. The slide on the screen read 'WHAT IS SPLASHASOAP'S LOGICO-PSYCHOLOGICAL PROPOSITION?' It wasn't moving, so answer came there none. Snap snap, snap snap, snap snap. Bernie's raised arm sounded like a cap-gun.

Suddenly a voice echoed round the room. A disembodied, irascible voice, resonant with fury, like the voice of doom. 'Stop snappin' yer bleedin' fingers at me,' it boomed. 'The bleedin' projector's jammed. I'll fix it in a minute, if you stop snappin' yer fingers. I don't like it. I'm not yer dog.' It was Albert, in his projection room, talking to himself, having forgotten to switch off the intercom system.

Instantly Flora scuttled to the projection room, switched the sound off and the lights on, and there was temporary hubbub while everyone from Pendletons except Tom Nathan and Paul O'Reilly apologised profusely and repeatedly, until as if of its own accord the slide on the screen changed to read, faintly in the light: 'SPLASHASOAP'S MOISTURISING EFFECTS OFFER WOMEN THE POWER TO CONTROL AGEING.'

'That's absurd,' muttered the Chairman to himself, as Bernie Barnstaple hurriedly returned to the lectern. The lights were dimmed again and he recommenced, his hands hanging limply at his sides, and forgetting to wave his spectacles about.'

'... so we've come a long way from our simple 3-S proposition "gunge and grime go away" and with Mr Greg Hamilton's marvellous help,' his voice was now heavy with sarcasm, 'arrived at a marvellous logico-psychological sales pitch. In case you haven't got it, the moisturising effect is the logical bit, the power to control ageing is the psychological bit. Very deep, you see. Now I'll hand you back to Flora.'

'To Dave Horrell,' Flora corrected him.

'To Dave Horrell,' Bernie concurred, already walking back to his seat. It was Dave Horrell's job to present the agency's media recommendations.

Dave knew, as everyone in the advertising business knows, and indeed as Irving Gilbernetti had so pungently stated a few days earlier, that the media recommendations sections of agency new business presentations are, invariably, soporifically boring. In the first place every agency in the land claimed to buy space in the press and magazines, and spots on television and radio, much more cheaply than every other agency in the land. As this is an arithmetic impossibility, everyone also knows that most agencies must be lying, but nobody knows which. Not even the agencies themselves, all of whom believe – had to believe – in their own media-buying prowess.

In the second place the media recommendations inevitably comprise a long series of complex computer analyses showing which publications (from the thousands available) and which television time-slots (from the thousands available) would reach the target audience most cost-effectively. Whether these analyses are transmuted into pretty graphs, or pie charts, or left as columns of figures, makes little difference. Only a tiny minority of human beings, like Marvyn Gottlieb, find bundles of figures a bundle of fun.

In the third place, and most boring of all, because computers are not imbued with much capricious imagination, they all promulgate similar results, and so clients visiting several agencies for new business presentations receive from each of them – at the end of the endless analyses – much the same proposals.

Being well aware of these problems Dave Horrell was today determined to overcome them. 'I am not,' he announced as he reached the lectern, 'going to bore you with lots of figures. Larsons have been working with Pendletons for long enough for you to know that when we promise to buy more cheaply than any other agency in town we mean it. And we deliver.'

Tom Nathan gazed at his agency's Media Director with a mixture of affection and despair. Dave Horrell, who lived in Weybridge and went to guitar lessons each Tuesday and Friday evenings, was wearing one of his loud kipper ties, clumsily knotted. His powder-blue suit was at least a couple of sizes too big for him and his shoes were scuffed. Tom's own sartorial untidiness was calculated: the right image, he believed, for a talented creative man. Dave was simply a mess. He was also, Tom was certain, slightly inebriated as usual.

'You will find,' Dave was continuing, 'our full media recommendations in the document which . . . ' he turned questioningly to Simon Booth, 'they'll be given at the end of the presentation, won't they?'

'Oh yes. Definitely. I think.'

'So I'll just make one vital point. As one of London's major agencies,' Dave – though a trifle befuddled – knew they were now competing only with the tiny and unsuccessful GOB shop, 'Pendletons has big media muscle. Whatever they'll tell you to the contrary, small agencies don't stand a chance against the Murdochs and the Maxwells, less still against Thames and Granada and all the other ITV companies. That lot are big, and they're tough. So if you're going to get the best deals today you need to be a big buyer, and you need to have the killer instinct . . . .'

Suddenly, without warning, he drew a pistol from his pocket and pointed it straight at Des Digby. His startled colleagues were dumbfounded. For God's sake, what was he up to? Was it a toy? It didn't appear to be. They all hated Des Digby, blamed him for their present predicament, but . . . 'You've got to let people know you'll stop at nothing, if they get in your way . . . ' Everyone in the room was now silent, motionless, mesmerised. 'You've got to let them know you've got *fire-power* – and you're ready to use it!'

Still aiming at Des Digby, he pulled the trigger. The starting pistol's blast was deafening. People's hands shot instinctively, protectively, belatedly to their ears as the explosion reverberated round the room.

Dave Horrell grinned boyishly, delighted at the disbelieving amazement he had provoked. No question about it: they weren't bored. It was an idea he'd had long ago, but had never before dared use. Had Chris Beaumont been present or had he been utterly sober he might, once again, have been deterred. But Larsons wouldn't forget his presentation in a hurry, that was for sure. 'And at Pendletons our fire-power is second to none,' he concluded, his audience still speechless.

'Thank you, ladies and gentlemen, for your kind attention.'

'That was a bloody stupid thing to do, Dave,' Des Digby expostulated as Horrell regained his seat at the back of the room. 'Those things can be dangerous.'

Flora hurried to the lectern to allay further disquiet.

'I'm sure Dave meant no harm, and . . . no harm's been done . . . Well, that certainly took us all aback, Dave . . . So now let's get on with the creative presentation. Francis?'

Thank God I won't be working in this madhouse much longer, Francis Kemp-Lewis thought, as he took a deep breath and briefly introduced Tom Nathan and Paul O'Reilly. 'They are undoubtedly one of London's top young creative teams,' he said, 'some would say *the* top young creative team, and we're delighted to have them here at Pendletons – if I may so boast on behalf of the agency.' The years of loyalty could not easily be sloughed off.

It was Tom Nathan's big break, and he did not intend to fluff it. He ran rapidly through the arguments that he had first advanced weeks before when he presented the Smashin' campaign to Chris Beaumont and the rest of them. The advertising was what the clients had come to see. Everything else was guff and waffle. His audience, with one exception, was listening attentively.

Flora Thompson was not listening. Her thoughts wandered from the presentation to Chris, and to Chris's wife. Ever since the phone call she had been unable to concentrate fully on the proceedings: she felt dazed and guilt-ridden, as if she were herself to blame, though she knew that to be ridiculous, irrational. She wondered where Chris was. What he was doing, how he was coping. What if his wife died? What would he do then? How would it affect her? How she wished she had been sensible, allowed logic to control her psychology, had stuck to her principles and kept clear of married men.

'... so I'll now show you an animatic of our launch commercial, an' then I'll explain it a bit more.'

For a few seconds which seemed like eternity to their bruised and battered eardrums, an unscheduled high-pitched screech emanated from two television screens, one either side of the room, and when eventually it stopped a neatly handdrawn commercial, with everything made from cardboard cut-outs, like cardboard dolls, began. A beautiful cartoon girl moved through the cartoon Cotswolds, in the cartoon rain, while the sound-track played a synthesiser and drums rock 'n roll orchestration of the *Pastoral* symphony. (Beethoven, Peter Dalrymple thought, would be spinning dizzily in his grave). Cartoon lightning flashed through the cartoon clouds, as the voice of a famous actor – who was it? – solemnly intoned through the music 'Plants need moisture, lots of moisture to keep fresh and healthy, and your hands need moisture too....'

But at that point, instead of the girl slipping in the mud, a tiny cartoon kitten appeared, soaked and muddy, and the girl picked it up, sheltering it from the storm, and there was a softfocus dissolve to a cute cartoon Cotswold cottage which the kitten instantly recognised and leapt towards. Next to the house was the beautiful Victorian water pump, the lightning illuminated the Splashasoap pack, the beautiful girl washed the moggy's mud off her hands, and the famous actor – who the hell was he? – continued: 'Splashasoap . . . keeps your skin soft as a kitten's coat', the lightning struck the pack and – despite Bernie Barnstaple's protracted and strenuous objections – it exploded, as before.

'I 'ope the imagery is clear,' Tom said immediately the commercial ended. 'Wanna see it again?'

'Yes, please.' Peter Dalrymple, like Chris Beaumont before him, had no idea what to make of it, but was fairly sure it was self-indulgent rubbish.

'From the top, Albert,' Tom called to the projectionist.

'Let's 'ave it two more times.'

'It's certainly original,' said the Chairman after the third showing.

'Is it essential to blow up the pack like that at the end?' asked Peter Dalrymple.

'No question,' Tom replied, 'that's what makes it so memorable, eh Pauly?'

Paul O'Reilly was far too nervous to answer.

'I say,' inquired the Chairman whimsically, 'what colour is the kitten?'

'Does it matter?' Tom detested smug, supercilious upper-class dilettantes within management, and his agressive response showed it.

'It's merely that there seem to be felines in all the commercials we've been seeing. An *embarras des chats,* as the Frogs would say. The last one was silver, I remember. I think they were going to paint it.'

Peter Dalrymple could restrain himself no longer. 'You're not supposed to tell one agency about another's proposals. That's the . . . convention . . . sir,' he added belatedly.

'Really? Can't see why not. Still, if it's not the done thing you'd better cross my remarks from the records, as they say. Hope I haven't blotted my copy book.'

'Will we be able to make that final claim?' Des Digby asked as soon as he felt he could. 'It's very strong, but will it get past the rule book?'

'Why not?' Tom replied. 'It's just a simile. 'Oo can say 'ow soft a kitten's coat is?'

'I've always thought kittens scratch,' said the Chairman, 'but then I'm a dog man myself. Beagles, you know. Anyway I like it. And I've always been told you can't go wrong with babies and kittens.'

'Everyone loves kittens,' Paul O'Reilly finally piped up.

'Oh, quite so,' the Chairman agreed, 'I'm just a boring old fart, so don't take any notice of me. Shouldn't be here really. Advertising's not my game, is it Peter? But I like it. Very much. A bit different. I'm sick to death of all those dreary soap adverts with housewives in kitchens telling each other how wonderful the product is.'

* * *

Ralph Isaacs was far from happy, not that that marked much of a change in his normal demeanour. Happiness was a condition he seldom thought about, did not find especially admirable, and anyway never associated with himself. The mercurial ambition by which he drove himself left him relaxed only when he was exhausted, only gleeful in fleeting, volatile moments of success. And for over ten days now successes had been irritatingly elusive. (Jonathan had even beaten him at chess a couple of times, and he was finding it increasingly difficult to accept even such trivial defeats gracefully.)

Like a crummy Piccadilly Circus neon ad, the Pendletons deal kept switching on–off. His cousin was still optimistic, he himself less sanguine. Although Pendletons' price had dropped by $100 million or so it was still absurdly high; and their inflated views of their agency's value reflected their inflated views of themselves. The more he learned about Pendletons – and he had never met anyone from the agency, nor had he the slightest intention of doing so – the more edgy he felt about the acquisition. The price would need to fall a good deal further before the risks were worth taking.

On a comparatively diminutive scale, ACM had pulled out of negotiations after winning Unigamble, Kelly was making no headway filching GOB's clients, while Isaacs and Isaacs shares had slid back twelve pence because an inane financial journalist had written an uninformed feature claiming they were overextended and had run out of steam. Ever since they had started journalists had been saying they were over-extended and had run out of steam. To Ralph the notion of running out of steam was, like happiness, utterly foreign. He was in the process of building the world's largest advertising agency, an agency – bigger even than the mammoth Japanese Dentsu corporation – that would last for two or three hundred years. There must somehow be a way of devising a corporate structure which was inherently as self-critical, as discontented, as perfectionist as he was himself; what was needed was a constitution like the Americans have, which would enshrine his beliefs in perpetuity. He would get Jonathan onto the task immediately.

But that was in the future, and today Isaacs and Isaacs was still unacceptably far from being the world's largest agency. Dentsu was more than twice as big, and that gnawed at Ralph's vitals. Suddenly an outrageous inspiration flashed through his mind. Why not buy Dentsu? At least try to? If he succeeded Isaacs and Isaacs would leap-frog straight to the world's number one spot; even if he failed he would learn a great deal about the structure of the world's number one agency in the process. Nobody had bought a major Japanese corporation before, ever; making the bid would itself take Isaacs and Isaacs onto the front pages of the world's media; and it would put the squeeze on Pendletons, once they learned he had another – and far, far mightier – iron in the fire.

'Come in here a minute, will you,' Ralph picked up the telephone and peremptorily summoned his cousin.

Strictly Private and Confidential

Dear Chris,
As you have been away I wanted to write to explain the background behind our decision to move our business to Gilbernetti, Orr and Burton.

Firstly, let me emphasise that it had nothing whatsoever to do with your departure and absence from the presentation. Your team put up a splendid show and we were all tremendously impressed by the radical approach Pendletons had taken, and by the creative work put up by your new young pair. They're obviously highly talented, if a mite unconventional, and I pray that our decision to move our business in no way reflects upon their future careers.

The facts of the matter, and I must ask you to keep this confidential at this time, as I know you will, are the Chairman has decided, after having seen the agency presentations and also a battery of computer projections of sales and profitability over the next five years, that we can no longer afford to advertise Splashasoap.

As you know it has been losing money since its launch, and a break-even point is nowhere in sight. We had hoped, perhaps a trifle over-optimistically, that the agency presentations would persuade us that some further investment would be worth while, but in the event this proved not to be so. We shall not, however, be withdrawing the brand, simply withdrawing TV advertising support.

Our decision to move to Gilbernetti, Orr and Burton was therefore predicated on the fact that our advertising account, which will be much smaller, would not be sufficient to command a major agency such as Pendletons' total commitment. Horses for courses as they say! In addition, it is perhaps fair to them to add, your competitors put up some interesting (and inexpensive!) high-class promotions which will not involve advertising per se.

Let me at this point put on record our sincere gratitude for all Pendletons have done for us during the term of your appointment. Please convey our appreciation to all concerned.

Finally I was most delighted to hear that your wife is recovering so well. Please pass to her my best wishes, together with those of all her friends here at Larsons.
Yours sincerely,

Peter Dalrymple

OUTSIDER GOB SCOOPS
£6 MILLION LARSONS

Campaign headline, early November